LIGHT VELOCITY
AND
RELATIVITY

by
ARTHUR S. OTIS, Ph.D.

Fellow of the American Association
for The Advancement of Science

THE PROBLEM OF LIGHT VELOCITY
EINSTEIN THEORY FOUND INVALID
A CLASSICAL THEORY OF RELATIVITY
A CHALLENGE TO YOUNG SCIENTISTS

Third Edition

LIGHT VELOCITY AND RELATIVITY

by ARTHUR S. OTIS, Ph.D.

THIRD EDITION

Published by

CHRISTIAN E. BURCKEL and ASSOCIATES

YONKERS-ON-HUDSON, N.Y.

Printed in the United States of America

by

UNIVERSAL LITHOGRAPHERS

Baltimore, Md.

Bound by

MOORE & CO., INC.

Baltimore, Md.

Library of Congress Catalog Card Number 63-15608

Dewey Decimal Classification Number 530.11

Price $5.00

CONTENTS

iii

THE AUTHOR

Excerpts from Who's Who In America

Ph.D. degree, Stanford University, 1920.

Instructor at Stanford University, and later at New York University, in the mathematics of research.

Advisor to the Surgeon General during World War I and originator of the method of intelligence testing by which 1,700,000 draftees were tested.

Author of the Otis Intelligence Tests by which fifty million individuals have been tested in both hemispheres.

Mathematics Editor of World Book Co. (25 years).

Educational Consultant for the U.S. Navy during World War II.

Psychological and Aeronautical Consultant for the Civil Aeronautics Administration.

Fellow of the American Association for the Advancement of Science since 1925.

Member: Sigma Xi, New York Academy of Sciences, American Physical Society, American Psychological Association, Institute of the Aeronautical Sciences, etc.

Author of books on mathematics, psychology, economics, aeronautics, etc.

(See also International Who's Who, American Men of Science, et.al.)

PREFACE

Scope of the booklet. The purpose of this preface is to present the scope of the booklet — its general purposes and the means employed to accomplish them.

An unsolved problem. The initial purpose of this booklet is to bring to the attention of young physicists and astronomers a problem of light velocity which the author regards as unsolved, in the hope that they will be challenged to solve it. Briefly stated, the problem is to make a choice among the three theories of light velocity described on page 1 — 'ether theory', the 'source theory', and the Einstein theory of relativity.

The Einstein theory. The quest for the solution of the problem immediately involves a critical analysis and evaluation of the Einstein (special) theory of relativity because, in a certain sense, the Einstein theory presumes to harmonize the evidence supporting the 'ether theory' with that supporting the 'source theory', by postulating that 'the velocity of light is constant', meaning that regardless of how a source of light and an observer may move relative to the cosmos, the velocity of the light from that source is the same relative to the source, relative to the cosmos, and relative to the observer.

The expression Einstein theory refers in this booklet to the so-called special theory of relativity as distinguished from Einstein's general theory of relativity — discussed in the Appendix.

Postulates of the theory. The fundamental postulates upon which the Einstein theory is based are as follows:

1. The relativity of motion. All uniform motion in a straight line is purely relative. There is no possibility of our distinguishing any unique straight-line motion that may be called absolute motion. If a train is in uniform motion relative to the ground we must consider that the ground is equally in motion relative to the train.

2. The uniform laws of nature. The laws of nature are the same in all inertial systems (frames of reference moving relative to one another in straight lines at uniform rate). This means, for example, that any phenomenon that takes place on the ground will take place in exactly the same way on a uniformly moving train.

3. The constant velocity of light. The velocity of light as measured by any observer will be found to have one and only one value (a 'universal constant') under all circumstances; that is, regardless of the motion of the source relative to the observer. Or, more succinctly: *The velocity of light is constant in all inertial systems.*

(The first two of these postulates are sometimes regarded as two aspects of the same postulate, and the third one is then referred to as Einstein's 'second postulate'.)

Acceptable postulates. We may regard as quite acceptable Einstein's postulate that all straight-line motion is relative only (no absolute motion can be detected) and his postulate that the laws of nature are the same in all inertial systems* including the laws governing the propagation of light.

It is only the postulate of the constant velocity of light to which the classicist need take exception.

Postulate based on mistaken reasoning. It is shown in Section 3 that the postulate of the constant velocity of light was set forth as the result of mistaken reasoning and that corrected reasoning shows that the postulate was not needed in the first place.

A case in point. To illustrate postulate 3 of the Einstein theory, let us suppose that at an instant, which let us call instant 0, a beam of light is emitted at a point A, stationary on the ground, and that at instant 1, one second later, the beam has reached point B, 300,000 kilometers from A. The velocity of the beam relative to the ground is 300,000 km. per sec.

```
       100,000                         300,000
   C———————————A————————————————————————————————B
                       400,000
```

Now let us suppose that during that same interval from instant 0 to instant 1 an observer moves from A to C, in the direction opposite to that of the motion of the beam. Let AC be 100,000 km. The velocity of the observer relative to the ground is 100,000 km. per sec.

Shall we not say, therefore, that the velocity of the beam relative to the observer is 400,000 km. per sec.?

Yet according to the Einstein theory that velocity is only 300,000 km. per sec.

Definition of relative velocity. By definition, the velocity of any thing relative to an observer is the distance by which the observer and the thing become separated (or brought nearer together) by their com-

*Inertial systems. The expression, inertial system, refers to any frame of reference, such as the cosmos, regarded as at rest, or such as a train moving at a uniform rate in a straight line. (A laboratory may be regarded as an inertial system when thought of as moving through the cosmos at a uniform rate in a straight line during any brief period.)

bined motions in one second. In the above illustration the combined motions of the beam and observer resulted in their being separated in one second by the distance 400,000 km. That is, by the definition of relative velocity, the velocity of the beam relative to the observer is 400,000 km. per second — not 300,000 km. per second as postulated by Einstein.

Einstein postulate disproved. Thus we see that in accord with the definition of relative velocity (and in accord with the classical concept that time is universal and a second is a second everywhere and everywhen) a beam of light can have one velocity relative to its source and another velocity relative to an observer who is moving relative to the source.

To the classicist (one who believes in the universality of time) this demonstration is sufficient to invalidate the Einstein concept of the 'constant velocity of light'.

In Section 2, two further disproofs of the postulate are given.

Nature of the theory. Although Einstein writes as if he would say that in the above illustration the velocity of the beam relative to the observer IS only 300,000 km. per sec., the same as its velocity relative to its source, nevertheless, as fully explained in the text, we must infer from the mathematics of the theory and from Einstein's discussion of the "behavior of measuring rods and clocks in motion" that according to the theory it is merely because of a peculiar behavior of measuring rods and clocks that the observer would obtain a measure of distance CB and a measure of the time interval that would cause the velocity of the beam relative to him to *come out* only 300,000 km. per sec. even though another observer standing at point A would find by measuring AB and AC that the velocity of the beam relative to the observer was actually 400,000 km. per sec.

Essentially a mathematical theory. It should be understood that the Einstein theory is essentially a mathematical theory. That is, it provides a pair of basic equations, called transformation equations (p. 32) which, when applied to measurements of time and distance made by one observer, tell us according to the theory what the measurements of the same time and distance would be if made by an observer moving relative to the first observer — it being assumed by the theory that two such observers would obtain differing measurements of the same time and distance.

Applying the equations to the measurements in the above illustration, it is presumed by the theory that the 'moving observer' would find by measurement that the distance CB was not 400,000 km. but 400,-000k km. (k equaling 1.06) and that the time interval was not 1 second but 4/3 k seconds, and that this observer would therefore find the velocity of the beam relative to him to be 400,000k kilometers in 4/3 seconds, or 300,000 kilometers per second — the same as its velocity relative to its source.

In brief, what the mathematical manipulations do is merely to assign a revised time interval to the motion of the beam relative to the 'moving observer' *in proportion* to the distance moved by the beam relative to the 'moving observer' so that the velocity of the beam relative to the 'moving observer' will come out the same as its velocity relative to its source.

Additional assumptions. In addition to the three basic postulates upon which the theory is presumed to rest there are embodied in the theory several additional assumptions, such as:—

(1) a measuring rod in motion is contracted,

(2) a clock in motion runs more slowly,

(3) events that are simultaneous for a stationary observer are not simultaneous for a moving observer, etc.

Einstein theory explained. The manner in which the 'behavior of measuring rods and clocks in motion' is presumed by Einstein to cause any observer to obtain one and only one value of the velocity of light, whether the source moves relative to him or not, is explained in great detail in this booklet. It is shown, for example, just why Einstein tells us that a meter in motion is shortened and a clock in motion runs more slowly than one at rest. A careful analysis of the basic equations of the theory reveals the surprising fact (not generally understood) that we are obliged to consider according to the theory that if the clocks along a train are in synchronism when it is at rest, the clocks all get out of synchronism when the train moves—all read differently when the train is in any given position. (In order to maintain that the clocks are not out of synchronism in such a case, Einstein merely redefines simultaneity, as explained in this booklet.)

It develops also that in order that an observer may obtain the same value of the velocity of a beam, whether the source moves relative to him or not, the observer is required by the theory to time the beginning of the motion of the beam by one clock and time the end of the motion by

---

* The curvature of light rays, advance of the perihelion of Mercury, etc., are mentioned by Einstein in connection with the general theory, not the special theory, with which this booklet deals. The general theory is treated at length in a forthcoming volume by the author.

another clock that is not in synchronism with the first. This is called the *two-clock method* of timing, and its requirement is fully explained.

The alleged confirmation of the special theory rests to a large extent upon the behavior of charged particles in electric and magnetic fields*, especially the diminishing acceleration of a charged particle in a cyclotron, whose electric and magnetic fields maintain constant strength. Einstein has deduced from his special theory that as the velocity of a particle increases, its mass increases. The diminishing acceleration of a charged particle in a cyclotron is generally believed to result from an an increase in its mass accompanying its increase in velocity; and it is generally considered that this phenomenon confirms the Einstein theory.

It is shown in this booklet, however, that mere relative velocity cannot have any effect upon the mass of a body and that the seeming increase in mass in the special case of a charged particle being accelerated in an electric field can be accounted for in terms of increased energy and that apart from such an increase in energy we may assume a body to have a constant mass regardless of its motion. Hence the seeming increase in mass of a charged particle cannot be cited as confirming the Einstein theory.

It is shown also that Einstein's reasoning by which he presumed to show that the Fizeau experiment with light in a flowing liquid confirmed his theory was fallacious and that consequently that experiment did not confirm his theory.

An irrational theory. It is shown in this booklet that the following are among the consequences of the theory.

1. If two beams of light from the same source move in opposite directions, each with the velocity c relative to the source, the velocity of one beam *relative to the other* is not $2c$, as we would expect, but only c.

2. If two marbles, A and B, were able to move away from each other with the velocity c (of light), for marble A marble B would be collapsed into a disk of zero thickness but would have infinite mass; and for marble B marble A would have zero thickness and infinite mass!

3. When a train at rest starts to move, its clocks immediately get out of synchronism in the sense that when the train is in any given position its clocks all read differently. The faster the train moves the further out of synchronism its clocks get.

4. The motion of a beam must be timed by timing the start of its motion by one clock and the end of its motion by another clock that is out of synchronism with the first clock.

5. The acceleration of a train causes the clocks in one portion of the train to speed up and the clocks in another portion of the train to slow down or *even run backward*.

6. Clocks must show intelligence in knowing whether to speed up or slow down under a given circumstance.

7. It is possible for an infinite series of events that occur in succession on the ground to occur simultaneously on a moving train — or *even in the reverse order*.

The classicist regards these consequences as irrational and hence rendering the theory unacceptable.

An impossible theory. Any theory that has contradictory consequences is an impossible theory. It is shown in this booklet that the Einstein theory leads to contradictory consequences — such as that the clocks on a train are both in synchronism and out of synchronism, or that one of two clocks in a moving train reads both earlier and later than the other. Because of these contradictions the author regards the theory as an impossible one. And if a theory is impossible to begin with, any discussion of alleged confirmations of the theory is futile because an impossible theory cannot be valid no matter how much evidence is advanced to support it.

A classical theory of relativity. Since the author finds no conflict between the 'principle of relativity' (the uniform laws of nature) and the concept of the universality of time, which Einstein was obliged to renounce in his theory, a 'classical theory of relativity' is presented in this booklet which combines the principle of relativity with the concept of the universality of time.

The challenge. It is shown in the beginning of Section 1 that there are two incompatible theories of the velocity of light — one called the *ether theory*, according to which the motion of a source of light relative to the cosmos is *not* imparted to its beams; hence the velocity of light is constant relative to an ether* — the other called the *source theory*, according to which the motion of a source relative to the cosmos (or any inertial system) *is* imparted to its beams; hence the velocity of light is constant relative to its source.

We may say that in a sense the Einstein theory attempted to harmonize these two mutually contradictory theories, which was, of course, impossible. The question still remains unanswered: Is the motion of a source of light imparted to its beams or not? If a source of light moves uniformly in a straight line in the cosmos, does the center of an expanding wavefront move with the source (so that the successive wave-

---

*We usually speak of 'the ether', referring to the hypothetical medium of the transmission of light—considered as stationary in the cosmos.

fronts are concentric), or does the center remain stationary in the cosmos (so that successive wavefronts are not concentric).

It is to be hoped that this booklet will challenge young scientists (particularly young physicists and astronomers) to help solve the problem of light velocity. Suggestions for further experiments which may help solve the problem are given.

Credit due. The author has no desire or intention to disparage in any way the truly scientific contributions of Dr. Einstein, particularly the one pertaining to the photo-electric effect, for which he was awarded the Nobel Prize. The purpose is merely to show that in the particular case of his special theory of relativity the author regards his writings as unscientific.

INTRODUCTION TO FIRST EDITION

The Einstein theory has seemingly gained the acceptance of scientists generally, and for that reason I had taken for granted that the theory was valid and well confirmed.

It was a great surprise to me, therefore, when Dr. Otis informed me that after six years of intensive study of the theory he had come to the conclusion that the theory is in need of substantial revision. This is so particularly because I have been well acquainted with Dr. Otis for forty years and have great respect for his keen analytical mind. He is known internationally for his pioneer work in the measurement of intelligence.

Dr. Otis has described to me in detail his method of evaluation of the theory as set forth in this brochure together with the reasons he finds a major portion of it unacceptable in spite of the seeming confirmations. I find no flaw in his reasoning and am obliged to agree with his findings. His presentation of the evidence of the spectroscope against the theory is most convincing.

It is true that many of the findings of science appear to be quite in accord with the theory and are generally regarded as confirming the theory. Dr. Otis has convinced me, however, that from the point of view of logic the fault of the theory is internal — that it has contradictory consequences that render it unacceptable in spite of the seeming confirmations. It seems very probable that the contradictory consequences that Dr. Otis has pointed out have escaped the attention of scientists, having come to light only as the result of a special graphic method of analysis that Dr. Otis has developed and which seems never to have been applied before to the theory.

It has often been said that the Einstein theory has required us to completely revise our ideas of time and space, adopting the concept of the relativity of time. Dr. Otis has shown that this is not at all necessary — that we can adhere to the time-honored concept of the universality of time.

Dr. Otis is a relativist — having accepted Einstein's concepts of the relativity of motion and the uniformity of the laws of nature; but he has combined these concepts with that of the universality of time to give us a classical theory of relativity which in my judgment will eventually gain acceptance in place of the Einstein theory.

Earl R. Glenn, Ph.D.

Formerly Professor of Physics and
Head of the Department of Science
Montclair State Teachers College
Montclair, New Jersey.

1. ETHER THEORY VS. SOURCE THEORY

The problem. We do not know the nature of light—whether it is a wave motion in a medium or a motion of particles. If the velocity of light were better understood, we might better understand the nature of light.

Three theories of light velocity. We may say that there are three theories of the velocity of light, which may be designated and described as follows.

1. The 'ether theory' according to which the velocity of light is constant relative to an ether, stationary in the cosmos.

2. The 'source theory' according to which there is no ether and the velocity of light is constant relative to its source.

3. The Einstein theory according to which the velocity of light is constant (a) relative to the cosmos, (b) relative to its source, and (c) relative to any observer.

Support for the theories. The ether theory appears to be supported by the evidence of double stars since light from them seems to come to us with the same velocity relative to the cosmos whether the star is approaching or receding.

The source theory is supported by the famous Michelson-Morley experiment of 1887 when interpreted as indicating that beams from a source on the earth (and hence moving in the ether) have velocities that are equal relative to the earth (and hence relative to their source) rather than equal relative to the cosmos (or ether).

The Einstein theory is generally considered as being in accord with both evidences.

Purpose of the Einstein theory. Indeed, it is often said that the Einstein theory is based upon the null result of the Michelson- Morley experiment (see p. 74), suggesting that Einstein's reason for propounding the theory was to satisfy his felt need to explain how light velocity could be constant relative to a medium of transmission (ether) and at the same time constant relative to its source (on the earth, moving in the medium).

Purpose of the booklet. As indicated above, this booklet is addressed primarily to young physicists, its purpose being:

(1) to point out that in the framework of the concept of the universality of time the ether theory and the source theory are mutually

contradictory and cannot be reconciled because the velocities of the beams from a given source cannot be equal both relative to an ether and relative to their source (if their source is moving in the ether); and consequently only one of these theories can represent reality.

(2) to show why the classicist regards the Einstein postulate of the constant velocity of light as disproven by scientific evidence;

(3) to explain clearly just how the Einstein theory presumes to show, for example, that if a source of light at rest on the earth sends out beams in different directions, the velocities of these beams will be found equal relative to the earth, by an observer on the earth, and at the same time will be found equal relative to a moving train by an observer on the train.

(4) to show that Einstein's attempt to explain the 'constant velocity of light' in terms of the behavior of clocks and rods in motion leads to consequences which the author finds unrealistic, rendering the theory unacceptable.

(5) to show that the Einstein theory, in attempting to embrace several contradictory concepts renders itself unacceptable by leading to impossible consequences — leaving the problem of light velocity unsolved;

(6) to show that the seeming increase in the mass of a particle with increase in its velocity — which is generally regarded as confirming the Einstein theory — can be explained in accord with the classical concept of the universality of time, and consequently does not confirm the Einstein theory;

(7) to evaluate some of the past experiments that have a bearing on the problem of light velocity and suggest additional ones:

(8) to present tentatively a classical theory of relativity based upon Einstein's postulates of the relativity of motion and the uniformity of the laws of nature, but based also upon the classical concept of the universality of time, and

(9) to challenge young physicists to attack the existing problem in the effort to discover whether the velocity of light is constant relative to an ether or relative to its source, and thus promote the discovery of the true nature of light.

Space-time graphs. The contrast between the ether theory and the source theory can be illustrated most effectively by means of a 'space-time graph.' Fig. 1-1 is a space-time graph. It represents the hypothetical motion of a long platform in space relative to a row of stars considered as stationary in the cosmos or ether.

2

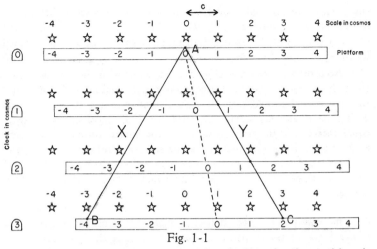

Fig. 1-1

The upper drawing represents the platform in the position in which its zero point is just opposite star 0, at an instant 0 (which we may think of as exact noon) when a clock in the cosmos reads 0, as shown at the left. The next drawing represents the platform as having moved a little to the right when the cosmos clock reads 1, (which we may think of as 1 second past noon). The next drawing represents the platform as having moved further to the right; and the bottom drawing represents the position of the platform when the cosmos clock reads 3, at which instant the zero point (origin) of the platform has moved the unit distance c to star 1. (c, as a distance, represents 300,000 kilometers; as a velocity, c represents 300,000 km. per sec.)

The figure is called a space-time graph because the horizontal dimension represents distance (space) and the vertical dimension represents time (measured downward).

The 'space-time line' AB represents the motion of a beam* of light X, emitted at star 0 at instant 0, which reaches star -1 in 1 second star -2 in 2 seconds, and star -3 in 3 seconds. Similarly space-time line AC represents the motion of a beam of light Y emitted simultaneously with beam X and which reaches star 1 in 1 second, star 2 in 2 seconds, and star 3 in 3 seconds.

Source theory vs. ether theory. The contrast between the ether theory and the source theory is shown in Fig. 1-2, which represents the same motion of a platform through the cosmos that is represented in Fig. 1-1. However, in Fig. 1-2 we suppose a source S of light to be stationary on

---

* A 'beam' of light may be thought of as single 'bullet of light' or photon.

3

the platform at its origin and hence moving in the cosmos (instead of stationary in the cosmos, as shown in Fig. 1-1.) The motion of the source S relative to the cosmos (ether) prior to instant 0 is represented by the space-time line SA.

According to the ether theory beams emitted in the two directions from the source on the platform at instant 0 would travel the 'space-time paths' AB and AC; and hence arrive at instant 3 at stars —3 and 3 (points B and C) having traveled equal distances in the ether in equal intervals; whereas, according to the source theory these beams emitted from the source moving in the cosmos would travel the space-time 'paths' AD and AE, arriving in 3 seconds at the points —3 and 3 of the platform, and hence traveling equal distances relative to their source.

Incompatible theories. It is clear that two beams emitted from the source S cannot travel 'paths' AB and AC and at the same time travel the 'paths' AD and AE. Hence the ether theory and source theory are mutually contradictory. Only one can represent reality.

The incompatibility of the two theories can be shown in several other ways.

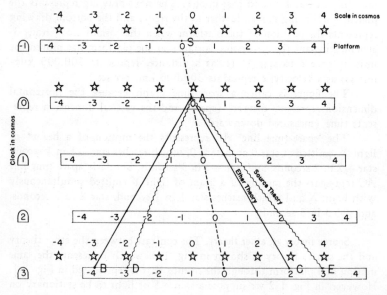

Fig. 1-2

A second contradiction. Let us say that at instant 0 beams are emitted at A (Fig. 1-2) from two sources — a source S that is stationary on the platform and hence moving in the cosmos, and a source S' that is stationary in the cosmos at star 0.

According to the source theory the beams from source S would travel the 'paths' AD and AE, as just explained, and the beams from source S' would travel equal distances from star 0 in 3 seconds, traveling 'paths' AB and AC.

On the other hand, according to the ether theory the beams from both sources would travel the 'paths' AB and AC, because according to that theory all beams have the same velocity in the ether no matter whether their source is stationary in the ether or moving in the ether.

Now it is clear that according to the source theory the rightward-moving beams from the two sources would diverge, following the diverging 'paths' AC and AE (and similarly for the two leftward-moving beams). However, according to the ether theory the two rightward-moving beams would travel side by side since both would travel the 'path' AC.

The contradiction between the two theories lies in the fact that two beams cannot both diverge and not diverge at the same time. Either the two beams diverge or they do not diverge. If the ether theory is true the source theory is not, and vice versa.

A third contradiction between the two theories lies in the fact that according to the ether theory the velocity of a source relative to the cosmos is *not imparted to the beams;* whereas, according to the source theory the motion of a source relative to the cosmos or any inertial system *is* imparted to the beams. (For example, 'path' AC in Fig. 1-2 represents the velocity (3 units in 3 seconds) of a beam relative to the cosmos when the velocity of the source is not imparted to it. 'Path' AE represents the velocity (4 units in 3 seconds relative to the cosmos) when the velocity of the source (1 unit in 3 seconds) has been imparted to the beam.

It is clear that the velocity of a source cannot be both imparted to its beams and not imparted to its beams. For a third reason, therefore, we must decide that the ether theory and source theory are incompatible.

Supplement 1. Three additional contradictions between the source theory and ether theory are given in Supplement 1 (p. 90).

Support for the ether theory. The principal support for the ether theory lies in the phenomena of reflection, refraction, diffraction, and polarization of light, all of which are explained most satisfactorily in terms of the wave theory, which conceives of light as a wave motion in an ether, presumably with a constant velocity in the ether.

Additional evidence supporting the ether theory is the absence of phenomena in astronomy (such as an apparent non-Keplerian orbital motion of binary stars) which would be expected in accord with the source theory.

Support for the source theory.* On the other hand the source theory is supported by measurements of the velocity of light relative to the earth which show no difference depending upon the motion of the source (earth) relative to the cosmos.

It is supported by the Michelson-Morley experiment, as indicated above, and supported by the Kennedy-Thorndike experiment. (See pp. 74 and 75.)

The source theory is supported also by all the evidence leading to the quantum theory, such as the photoelectric effect, the Compton effect, which suggests that light consist of particles which may be presumed to have a constant velocity relative to their source.

We might say that the source theory is supported by the concept of the uniform laws of nature according to which in any inertial system

---

***Qualifying the source theory.** When we say that according to the source theory the velocity of light is constant relative to its source, we mean, of course, provided the source continues to move in a straight line in the same direction and with the same velocity as when the light was emitted. In that case the source will always be at the center of any expanding wavefront. Otherwise, as when the source is following a curved path, the source will move away from the center of the wavefront and the velocities of the beams in the different directions from the source will not be equal relative to the source.

According to Einstein's postulate that the laws of nature are the same in all inertial systems, which is acceptable, it is reasonable to assume that in any inertial system in which there is a stationary mirror a light of any velocity will be reflected in the mirror with the same velocity it had before reflection: that is, in any inertial system the velocity of reflection equals the velocity of incidence relative to a stationary mirror.

But let us say a beam moves to the right with velocity c relative to a system S and is reflected to the left by a mirror moving to the left with velocity v relative to system S. According to the source theory the beam moves with the velocity $c + v$ relative to the mirror and relative to the system S' in which the mirror is at rest. Upon reflection it moves again with the velocity $c + v$ relative to the mirror (and system S') but now with the velocity $c + 2v$ relative to system S, in which the source is at rest. Hence 'constant relative to its source' means *before reflection in any moving mirror.*

Stated most precisely, therefore, the concept of the 'source theory' is that the velocity of any beam, as emitted from its source and before reflection, is constant relative to the inertial system in which the source was at rest (and with which it is moving) at the instant the beam is emitted. (In any inertial system in which the source is at rest when the beam is emitted the velocity of the beam will be c after reflection from any number of stationary mirrors.)

6

we would expect the velocities of beams from a source in that system to be constant. For example, thinking of the earth as an inertial system, it would follow according to the ether theory that the velocities of beams from a source at rest in that system would be different relative to the system in the different directions; whereas, thinking of the cosmos as an inertial system, according to the ether theory the velocities of beams from a source at rest in that system would be the same in all directions. Thus, according to the ether theory we would have unequal velocities in one system and equal velocities in another system — contrary to the concept of the uniform laws of nature in all inertial systems; whereas according to the source theory the velocities of the beams would be the same in both systems and this is in accord with the concept of the uniform laws of nature.

Additional support for the ether theory and for the source theory is discussed later in the booklet (see pages 75, 76, 77 and 79.)

2. DISPROOF OF THE CONSTANT-VELOCITY POSTULATE

Disproof of the constant-velocity postulate. It was shown in the Preface that Einstein's postulate of the 'constant velocity of light', interpreted literally, is contrary to the definition of relative velocity. The classicist regards this postulate as disproven by the phenomenon of the aberration of starlight, in accord with the following reasoning.

Aberration. Let the line AB in Fig. 2-1 represent the path of a beam of light decending vertically from a star. Let the line CB represent the direction of motion of the earth's surface and hence the direction of motion of an observatory and its telescope. Let us suppose the telescope to be adjusted to observe the star and that just at the instant the beam reaches point A the telescope is in the position AC so that at that instant (instant A) the beam enters the telescope. Let us say that the telescope moves to the right during the decent of the beam so that just as the beam reaches point B (instant B) the eyepiece, moving along the line CB, also reaches point B. This means that during the interval from instant A to instant B the beam travels down the center line of the telescope.

One and only one interval. Now let us realize that the beam and the tip of the telescope arrive at point A at one and only one instant and that the beam and the eyepiece arrive at point B at one and only one instant. It follows, therefore, that the time of travel of the beam down the path AB relative to the cosmos and the time of travel of the beam down the center line AC or BD of the telescope are one and only one interval.

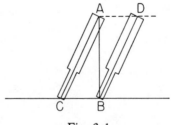

Fig. 2-1

Unequal velocities. Now the path CD traveled relative to the telescope in that one interval is longer than the path AB traveled relative to the cosmos; but if a beam travels two unequal distances in one and the same interval it does so at unequal velocities. That is, the velocity

8

of the beam relative to the telescope (as one inertial system) is greater than its velocity relative to the cosmos (as another inertial system). Thus we have a clear case of the velocity of a beam not being constant — not being the same in two inertial systems. The classicist considers this phenomenon to disprove the Einstein constant-velocity postulate.

Applying the theory. The question arises as to how the Einstein theory would presume to show that the velocity of the beam was the same in both paths. It does so quite simply. By the application of the so-called 'transformation equations' of the theory different travel times are assigned to the travel of the beam in the two paths. These assigned travel times have the same ratio as the ratio of the distances traveled in the two paths. Thus, if path AC is actually 1% longer than path AB the equations assign a travel time for path AC that is just 1% greater than the travel time assigned to the path AB. Of course, in accord with these newly assigned travel times the velocities in the two paths come out the same.

This of course, does not change the fact that, as shown above, the travel time in both paths was one and only one interval, and that during this one and only one interval the beam traveled farther relative to the telescope than it did relative to the cosmos and hence at greater relative velocity.

Section 4 describes in detail the manner in which the theory presumes to show by the application of its 'transformation equations' how and why the velocity of the beam is the same in both paths (p. 48.)

A device to illustrate aberration. In Supplement 5 (p. 102) directions are given for making and using a simple device to illustrate the aberration of star light as shown in Fig. 2-1. The reader will find it very illuminating and profitable to make this device which enables one to actually *see* the 'beam' descend the path AB and at the same time descend the center line of the telescope.

Evidence of the spectroscope. Further disproof of the Einstein constant-velocity postulate lies in the evidence of the spectroscope, which may be shown as follows.

Measuring the velocity of light. It is well understood that it is possible to measure the velocity of light relative to an observer in either of two ways.

9

One way is to divide the distance (d) traveled by the light by the time (t) taken by the light to travel the distance. The quotient is the velocity (V) of the light. That is, $V = d/t$.

The other way is to multiply the wavelength (w) of the light by the frequency (f) of its waves as received by the observer. The product (wf) is the measured velocity of the light relative to the observer. That is, $V = wf$.

Measurement of velocity itself not necessary. It is not necessary to measure directly either the wavelength or the frequency of reception of the light from a given source by an observer in order to determine whether the measured velocity of the light relative to the observer changes. That is, if the wavelength (w) of a given light is known to remain unchanged, and the frequency (f) of reception of the waves by an observer is known to change, it follows that the velocity (wf) of the light relative to the observer must change.

Experimental disproof of the Einstein postulate of the constant velocity of light. It is well understood that when there is relative motion between a star and a spectroscope, the spectrum of the star is shifted from its normal position. This is true whether the relative motion is caused by motion of the star toward or away from the spectroscope or by motion of the spectrscope toward or away from the star, or both.

Wavelength unchanged. Now it is clear that the motion of a spectroscope toward or away from a star, caused by the orbital and rotational motions of the earth, cannot in any way affect the *wavelength* (w) of the light of the star. This means that when these motions of the earth cause the spectroscope to approach a star, the shift of the spectrum of the star toward the violet clearly indicates an increase in the *frequency* (f) of the star light* as received by the spectroscope. And a shift of the spectrum toward the red, when the spectroscope recedes from the star clearly indicates a decrease in the frequency of the star light as received by the spectroscope.

Variable velocity of light. Now since velocity equals wavelength multiplied by frequency $(v = wf)$, it follows that when the wavelength of the light of a star is unchanged and its frequency of reception by the spectroscope changes, as indicated by the shift of the spectrum of of the light, the velocity (wf) of the light relative to the spectroscope changes.

* Considered as monochromatic — having one frequency.

Thus we may say that the shift of the spectrum of the light of a star actually observed — the shift being the result of the change of motion of the spectroscope relative to the star caused by the revolution and rotation of the earth — constitutes direct empirical evidence of the variability of the velocity of light relative to the spectroscope and relative to the observer, contrary to Einstein's postulate of the 'constant velocity of light,' according to which it is impossible to detect in any manner any change in the velocity of light relative to any observer, instrument, or inertial system.

No measuring rods or clocks involved. Einstein's explanation of an observer's always obtaining the same measure of the velocity of light is based upon a presumed "behavior of measuring rods and clocks in motion" (see Chapter XII in his *Relativity*). We must realize clearly, therefore, that an observation of the shift of the spectrum of a light (resulting from a change in the frequency of the light as received by a spectroscope because of a change of motion of the spectroscope relative to the source of light) does not involve measuring rods or clocks in any way. Thus we may say that we have an observation of the variability of the velocity of light relative to an observer that Einstein's concept of the behavior of measuring rods and clocks in motion cannot explain away.

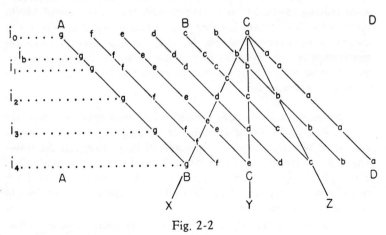

Fig. 2-2

Graphic representation. The above reasoning may be made clearer, perhaps, by means of a space-time graph. Thus, in Fig. 2-2 the letters *g f e d c b a* represent a train of wavefronts moving to the right. The distance from *a* to *b* is one wavelength (w). The figure represents the

11

six wavelengths as occupying at instant i_0 the distance from point A to point C. The train of waves moves one wavelength per unit of time so that at instant i_1 (1 unit of time later) wavefront b reaches point C, and so on, till by instant i_4 the train of waves occupies the distance between B and D. The parallel slanting space-time lines represent the continuous motion of the wavefronts.

Now let us suppose there is a spectroscope at point C. The graph shows that at instant i_4 wavefront e reaches the spectroscope; hence during the 4 units of time from instant i_0 to instant i_4 the spectroscope receives the 4 wavefronts b, c, d, and e. That is, the frequency of reception of the wavefronts by the spectroscope is 1 per unit of time.

Now let us say that instead of remaining at point C the spectroscope moves 2 wavelengths to the right during the interval i_0 to i_4, as represented by the space-time line Z. This line shows that during that 4-unit interval the spectroscope receives only the 2 wavefronts b and c— the frequency of reception being only $\frac{1}{2}$ wavefront per unit of time.

However, if we let the spectroscope move to the left as represented by the space-time line X, we find that during the 4-unit interval the spectroscope receives 6 wavefronts (b, c, d, e, f, and g)—the frequency of reception being $1\frac{1}{2}$ wavefronts per unit of time.

No change of wavelength. The graph shows that with the spectroscope moving to the left as indicated, wavefront b is received by the spectroscope at an instant i_b earlier than instant i_1; but it is clear that at instant i_b the wavelengths (ab, bc, etc.) are the same as when the spectroscope remains at C. Motion of the spectroscope changes the frequency of its reception of the wavefronts but such motion in no way changes the wavelengths.

Different relative velocities of light. The velocity with which the light is received by the spectroscope is represented, of course, by the number of wavelengths received per unit of time. (Suppose the wavelength were a centimeter and we called the unit of time a *sycond*. Then if the spectroscope received the waves with the frequency of say 5 per unit of time, the velocity of the light relative to the spectroscope would be 5 centimeters per sycond.)

Now we have already seen that when the spectroscope is stationary at C the velocity of reception is 1 wavelength per unit of time; whereas, when the spectroscope moves to the left as indicated, the velocity of reception of the wavelengths $1\frac{1}{2}$ wavelengths per unit of time. This shows that the velocity of the light relative to the spectroscope is different in the two cases.

12

Einstein postulate contradicted. As stated earlier, according to the Einstein postulate of the 'constant velocity of light' there is no way by which an observer can detect any difference in the velocity of light relative to him. Nevertheless we see that the shift of the spectrum of light when the spectroscope is moved toward the source provides us with definite empirical evidence that the frequency of reception of the wavefronts by the spectroscope is increased and hence (the wavelength remaining unchanged) the velocity of the light relative to the spectroscope (and relative to the laboratory and observer) is increased, thus contradicting the Einstein postulate.

Supplement 2 (p. 93) discusses attempts to refute the above reasoning regarding the evidence of the spectroscope in disproving the postulate of the 'constant velocity of light'. These will be better understood after Section 4 has been read.

Summary of Section 2. In this section it has been shown:

(1) that the postulate of the 'constant velocity of light' is disproven by reference to the definition of relative velocity, by the aberration of starlight, and by the evidence of the spectroscope, according to which a shift of a spectrum indicates a change in the frequency of reception of the wavefronts from a source of light relative to which the spectroscope is moving without affecting the wavelengths of the light — thus showing the velocity of the light relative to the spectroscope to be variable — not constant as postulated by Einstein;

(Supplement 2 shows that various attempts to explain how the approach of a spectroscope to a source of light could change the wavelength of the light are unconvincing to the classicist).

13

3. THE EINSTEIN THEORY EXPLAINED

Does the Einstein theory explain? As has been stated, the Einstein theory of light transmission presumes to harmonize the evidence supporting the ether theory with that supporting the source theory by presuming that beams in different directions from a given source all have the same velocity both relative to that source and relative to the cosmos.

But in the light of the contradictions explained above which prove that the velocities of beams from a given source moving in the ether cannot be equal relative to the ether and relative to their source, the question arises: How could the Einstein theory presume to harmonize these contradictory concepts?

Explanation of the Einstein theory. The manner in which Einstein presumes to demonstrate his postulate of the 'constant velocity of light' may be explained most clearly by means of space-time graphs.

Thus, Fig. 3-1 represents the motion of a train to the right past a row of trees. The top picture shows that at an instant which let us call instant 0 (shown by the clock at the left) the zero point (origin) of the train scale is just opposite tree 0. The next picture shows that at instant 1 (1 second later) the train has moved so that its origin is slightly to the right of tree 0. The next picture shows the origin of the train still further to the right; and the fourth picture shows that at instant 3 the origin of the train has reached tree 1.

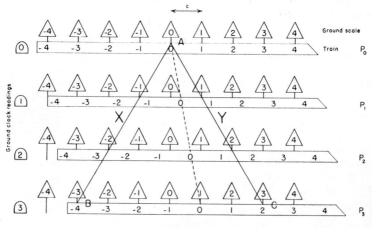

Fig. 3-1

14

Space-time lines. The space-time line AB represents the motion of a beam of light X which is emitted at tree 0 at instant 0 and which moves to the left, reaching tree -1 in 1 second, tree -2 in 2 seconds, and tree -3 in 3 seconds. Space-time line AC represents the motions of a beam Y that is emitted at tree 0 at instant 0 but which moves to the right with the same velocity, reaching tree 3 in 3 seconds.

An observer on the train. Now let us say there is an observer riding on the train at its origin. We see by the figure that at instant 3 beam X reaches tree -3 just as the -4 mark of the train scale reaches that tree, meaning that at that instant the beam is 4 units away from the observer who is at the origin (0 point) of the train. Also we see that at instant 3 beam Y has just reached the 2 mark of the train scale, showing that at that instant the beam is 2 units away from the observer on the train.

Velocities equal according to Einstein. It would seem clear from these considerations that in this case the observer on the train would find that the velocity of beam X relative to the train was 4 units in 3 seconds and that the velocity of beam Y relative to the train was 2 units in 3 seconds. However, according to Einstein the observer on the train would find that the velocities of both beams X and Y were 3 units in 3 seconds — the same as the velocities of these beams relative to the ground.

Basis of Einstein's reasoning. As stated above, it is generally understood that Einstein's reasoning was based primarily upon the result of the Michelson-Morley experiment which was believed to indicate quite definitely that the velocity of the light used in the experiment (which was from a terrestrial source) was the same in all directions relative to the earth and the source even though the earth is in motion.

First, we must remember that since in the Michelson-Morley experiment the source of light was at rest in the laboratory, we cannot conclude from that experiment anything regarding the velocity of beams relative to the earth when the beams have their source not at rest relative to the earth. Is it not mistaken reasoning, therefore, to assume that it follows from the Michelson-Morley experiment that the velocities of *all* beams must be the same relative to the earth whether these beams have their source at rest on the earth or not?

Let us consider the constant-velocity postulate also from the point of view of the concept of the uniform laws of nature.

Postulate based upon mistaken reasoning. It seems probable that Einstein's postulate of the 'constant velocity of light' is the result of mistaken reasoning. Here is why.

According to Einstein's postulate that the laws of nature are the same in all inertial systems it follows that beams from a *source on the ground* would have velocities that are *equal relative to the ground,* as represented by lines *AB* and *AC* in Fig. 1-2; whereas beams from a *source on the train* would have velocities that are *equal relative to the train,* is represented by lines *AD* and *AE**. The mistake Einstein appears have made is in thinking that from the above postulate it must follow also that beams from a *source on the ground* must have velocities that are *equal relative to the train.* This latter concept just doesn't follow at all from the postulate of the uniform laws of nature. Here is an analogy.

We know that if we stand still on the ground and drop a ball it will fall straight down to the ground. And we know, too, that if we stand still on a uniformly moving train and drop a ball it will fall straight down *relative to the train.* Indeed, this is the sort of phenomenon that has led us to believe that the laws of nature are the same in all inertial systems.

But because of these observations would we expect that a ball dropped by a person standing on the ground would fall straight down *relative to the train?* No! A ball that drops straight down relative to a train follows a curved path relative to the ground, *and vice versa.*

Now there is no more reason to assume (gratuitously) that beams from a source at rest on the ground will have velocities that are equal relative to the train than there is to assume that a ball dropped by a person on the ground would fall straight down relative to a train.

It would appear that if Einstein had properly distinguished between beams of light from a source on a train and beams from a source on the ground he would have realized that there is nothing about the uniform laws of nature that requires us to assume that beams from a source on the ground would have equal velocities relative to the train and that there was no need for him to postulate that beams from a source in a given inertial system have equal velocities in all inertial systems; but merely that they have equal velocities in the given system in which their source is at rest.

Postulate not needed. Thus we see that so far as the Michelson-Morley experiment is concerned, and so far as the concept of the uniformity of the laws of nature is concerned there was no need for the postulate of the 'constant velocity of light' in the first place.

*Thinking of the platform as a train and the stars as a ground scale.

Indeed, Einstein presents another reason for his adoption of the postulate of the constant velocity of light and this, too, is found to be in error. This is explained in Supplement 3, p. 96.

Ambiguous statement. It should be understood that the result of the Michelson-Morley experiment has often been stated ambiguously as indicating that "the velocity of light is constant regardless of the motion of its source." This statement is ambiguous because it can have either of two contradictory meanings.

Thus, the statement can mean:—

(1) the velocity of light is constant *relative to the ether* regardless of the motion of its source relative to the ether. Or it can mean:—

(2) the velocity of light is constant *relative to its source* regardless of the motion of its source relative to the ether.

The first of these statements expresses the ether theory and the second one expresses the source theory. It has been made clear that these concepts are mutually contradictory. Hence we must regard the statement that *the velocity of light is constant regardless of the motion of its source* as ambiguous and to all intents and purposes meaningless.

Whether or not Einstein was misled by this ambiguous statement, it would appear that his theory is an attempt to encompass both possible meanings of the statement.

Essence of the Einstein method. We have seen that in Fig. 3-1 if beams X and Y reached trees —3 and +3 in 3 seconds (position P_3), beam X would be 4 units from the origin of the train and beam Y would be 2 units from the origin of the train. The essence of the Einstein method of explaining why an observer on the train would obtain measurements indicating that the velocities of beams X and Y were equal relative to the train also is as follows.

Because at position P_3 beam X has traveled 4 units relative to the train Einstein merely assumes that because of certain peculiar behavior of the train clocks the observer will obtain 4 seconds as the travel time of that beam from A to B; whereas, in the case of beam Y (which has traveled only 2 units relative to the train), Einstein assumes that the observer will obtain only 2 seconds as the travel time of that beam from A to C. This would mean, of course, that the observer on the train found the velocity of each beam to be 1 unit per second*.

---

* The slight manner in which Einstein's method differs from this Simple Method will be explained later, at which time it will be seen that in no way does this Simple Method misrepresent the Einstein method.

The row of train clocks. Einstein says, in effect: Assuming that the train clock at the origin of the train reads 0 when the beams start (the train being in position P_o) I assume that there is a row of clocks along the train by which the time of arrival of the beams at any point on the train can be read. Since in this case we find that when the train is in position P_3 the beams arrive at the points —4 and 2 on the train, I assume that when the train is in this position the train clock at —4 reads 4 and the train clock at 2 reads 2, as shown at B and C in Fig. 3-2, and that the observer on the train will read the starting time of each beam as 0 by the clock where the beams start (as shown at A) and will read the arrival time of beam X at point B as 4, and the arrival time of beam Y at C as 2. He will then obtain the velocity of beam X as 4 units in 4 seconds and the velocity of beam Y as 2 units in 2 seconds — both these velocities being 1 unit per second and therefore equal velcities.

(This is the essence of the Einstein theory — the Einstein method of demonstrating the 'constant velocity of light'. The theory merely assigns travel times to beams in proportion to the distances traveled in the particular inertial system.)

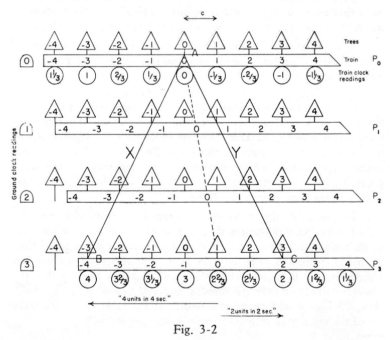

Fig. 3-2

Interpolation. Einstein then says, in effect: Since I assume when the train is in position P_3, that the train clock at —4 reads 4 and the

18

train clock at 2 reads 2, I assume by interpolation that the clocks stationed at the intervening points, -3, -2, -1, 0, and 1 will read $3\frac{2}{3}$ $3\frac{1}{3}$, 3, $2\frac{2}{3}$ and $2\frac{1}{3}$. (These readings are shown in the circles in the figure.)

He then says in effect: Since it develops that when the train is in position P_3 each train clock reads $\frac{1}{3}$ second later than the clock 1 unit in front of it, I infer that when the train was in position P_0 the same must have been true; that is, that the train clock at $+1$ read $-\frac{1}{3}$, the train clock at $+2$ read $-\frac{2}{3}$, etc., as shown in the circles.

Why the different clock readings? If we were to ask Einstein why he presumes that the clocks on the train will all read differently (as shown in Fig. 3-2) when the train is in position P_3, for example, his reply would be, in effect: I have to make this assumption in order to explain how the observer on the train could obtain the same velocity for the two beams relative to the train by his measurements. I have postulated that the observer will obtain the same velocity for the two beams, so I have to make this assumption of the different readings of clocks along the train with a reading of 4 at -4 and a reading of 2 at 2 and the intervening readings by interpolation.*

Slow running of train clocks. We note that according to the train clock readings presumed by Einstein, the clock at the zero point of the train reads 0 when the train is in the position P_0 and reads only $2\frac{2}{3}$ when the train is in the position P_3, although the ground clocks read 3. This indicates that according to the train clock readings presumed by Einstein the clock at the zero point of the train runs only 8/9 as fast as the ground clocks. Similarly it will be seen that according to the presumed readings each other train clock moves forward only $2\frac{2}{3}$ seconds while the ground clocks move forward 3 seconds.

Why the slower running of train clocks. If we ask Einstein how it can be that the train clocks run more slowly than the ground clocks in this case, his reply might be, in effect: Well, as you see, it works out that way; and I have found that no matter what the velocity of the train is, when I assign the appropriate readings to the different train clocks to make the velocities of the beams come out the same relative to the train, it always turns out that the train clocks have to be assumed to run more slowly than the ground clocks as in this case. In fact, I found that the faster the train goes the slower the clocks appear to run. So I have decided that for some reason when a train is in motion its clocks run more slowly than when it is at rest.

———
*See the heading. The appearance interpretation, page 21.

The two-clock method of timing. Considering that Einstein con-cedes that in the case of Fig. 3-2 each train clock moves forward only $2\frac{2}{3}$ seconds while the train moves from position P_0 to position P_3 and during the motion of the beams from tree 0 to trees -3 and $+3$, let us say we ask Einstein why, then, does he not take $2\frac{2}{3}$ seconds as the travel time the observer on the train would get for each of the two beams. He might reply in effect: If we did that the velocities of the two beams relative to the train would not come out the same. The velocity of beam X relative to the train would come out 4 units in $2\frac{2}{3}$ seconds and the velocity of beam Y would come out 2 units in $2\frac{2}{3}$ seconds— unequal velocities. But I have postulated that these velocities will come out equal as measured by the observer on the train. I have therefore made a rule to go with my theory, the rule being: The beginning of any motion must be timed by the clock where the motion begins and the end of the motion must be timed by the clock where the motion ends. I assume that the observer on the train will follow this rule. If he does he will time the start of beam X by the clock at 0 on the train and time the end of the motion of the beam by the clock at -4 on the train. He will then get a starting time of 0 and an arrival time of 4 and so get 4 seconds as the travel time of beam X. He will then find the velocity of the beam to be 4 units in 4 seconds or 1 unit per second. Also he will time the start of beam Y by the clock at 0 on the train and time its arrival at C by the clock at $+2$ on the train. He will thus get a starting time of 0 and an arrival time of 2 and get a velocity of 2 units in 2 seconds for that beam, which is also 1 unit per second, the same as for beam X. In short I have to assume that the observer on the train will use my rule; otherwise my explanation fails.

We might give the name 'two-clock method' to this method of timing the motion of a beam or other object.

An analogy. Let us suppose it is a 2-hour flight from Chicago to New York and a 4-hour flight from Chicago to Denver. Let us say we wish to make it appear that each of these flights is a 3-hour flight. It could be done by the two-clock method as follows.

We start each flight at Chicago at noon, Chicago time. One plane arrives in New York at 2 P.M., Chicago time, but it is then 3 o'clock by New York time. So if we time the start by Chicago time and time the arrival in New York by New York time we might then say that the plane flew from 12 o'clock to 3 o'clock and call the flight a 3-hour flight. The other plane arrives at Denver at 4 o'clock, Chicago time, but it is then only 3 o'clock, Denver time; hence using the same two-clock method we could say that this plane left at 12 and arrived at 3, making this flight also a 3-hour flight.

A 'classicist' (one who believes in the universality of time) considers this two-clock method of timing to be wholly fictitious and invalid, and cannot accept any theory that depends upon such a method.

The appearance interpretation. Followers of Einstein sometimes say that in a case such as that of Fig. 3-2, Einstein would not mean that the train clock readings indicated in the circles (such as 4, $3\frac{2}{3}$, $3\frac{1}{3}$, etc. for position P_3) were the actual readings the clocks would have at the instant the train is in that position; but that these are merely the readings the train clocks would *appear* to have at that instant to an observer on the ground — it being understood that to the observer on the train the train clocks would appear to be in synchronism.

This may be called the *appearance interpretation*, to which reference is made later. But it is a false and misleading interpretation. According to that interpretation Einstein would merely presume to demonstrate how the observer *on the ground* would find beams X and Y to have equal velocities relative to the train as well as relative to the ground — assuming he was able to read the train clocks as they went whizzing by, and assuming that he used the two-clock method!

But when Einstein proclaims that "the velocity of light is constant" he presumes to demonstrate by his theory that in a case such as that of Fig. 3-2, the observer *on the train*, measuring distances on the train and reading the train clocks as they actually indicate time, would find that the velocities of beams X and Y were equal.

Now it is impossible to make such a demonstration without assuming that the *actual* readings of the train clocks, as seen by the observer on the train, are all different at the instant the train is in any given position.

The reader can demonstrate this to his own satisfaction. Let him assume that the train clocks all appear to the observer on the train to be in synchronism. Let him choose any reading that the train clocks might be presumed by the theory to have when the train is in the position P_3, for example. Let us say he chooses the reading $2\frac{2}{3}$. Substituting that reading for the clock readings 4 and 2 at points B and C, the observer on the train, timing the start of each beam as 0 by the train clock at A, would find beam X to travel 4 units relative to the train (0 to -4) in $2\frac{2}{3}$ seconds, and would find beam Y to travel 2 units relative to the train (0 to $+2$) in $2\frac{2}{3}$ seconds. These, of course, are unequal velocities. Hence, as stated above, it is impossible to demonstrate how the observer on the train, reading the train clocks, could obtain equal velocities for beams X and Y unless it is assumed by the theory

21

that when the train is in any given poition, such as position P₃, the train clocks actually all read differently.

The author considers that the whole train and all its clocks occupy a given position at one and only one instant, and that if the train clocks all read differently at that instant they may properly be said to be out of synchronism.

Let it be remembered, therefore, that the *appearance interpretation* is false and misleading and cannot be invoked to explain away any contradiction arising in the application of the Einstein theory.

Summarizing so far, therefore, we may say that the special feature of the Einstein theory is the postulate of the 'constant velocity of light' according to which the velocity of the light issuing from a source on the ground will be the same in all directions relative to the ground; but according to which an observer riding on a moving train will find that the velocities of the beams from that source will be the same in all directions also relative to the train — particularly because of (1) an alleged peculiar behavior of clocks 'in motion', and (2) the use of a special rule of timing whereby the observer is presumed to time the beginning of a motion by a clock where the motion begins and to time the end of the motion by a clock where the motion ends — the two clocks not being in synchronism. The theory presumes that the readings of the row of clocks on the train when in any given position are such that when the two-clock method of timing is used, the travel times assigned to each beam will be *exactly in proportion* to the distances traveled by the beams relative to the train.

The transformation equations. We must regard the Einstein theory as essentially a mathematical theory based upon two fundamental equations called the 'transformation equations' (see p. 32). It is by one of these equations that the appropriate travel time of a beam relative to the train is presumed to be obtained so that its velocity relative to the train will come out the same as its velocity relative to the ground. When the equation is used, the fact that a two-clock method of timing is being used is completely obscured.

Opposite motion of the train. It is a simple matter to show that if the train in Fig. 3-2 were moving backward instead of forward, the Einstein theory and equations would require us to assume that the train clocks were out of synchronism in the reverse order, in the sense that when the train was in any given position each clock would read *earlier* than the one in front of it, as shown in Fig. 3-3, instead of *later* than the one in front of it, as in Fig. 3-2.

22

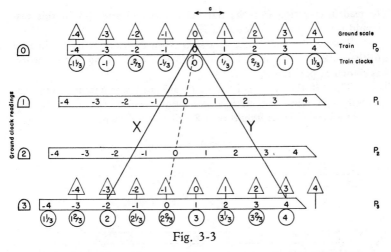

Fig. 3-3

It is clear why this reversed arrangement of the clock readings is required. Fig. 3-3 shows that when the train is in position P_3 beam X has moved only 2 units relative to the train — requiring the train clock to read 2 at −2 on the train, so that the train observer (using the two-clock method) will be presumed to get 2 seconds as the travel time of the beam, thereby presumably traveling 2 units in 2 seconds; whereas the train clock at +4 must be presumed to read 4 in order to make it appear that the motion of beam Y from A to C took 4 seconds.

Irregular progress of clocks. It is well known that the Einstein theory would assume that if the train in Fig. 3-2 were stationary relative to the ground the train clocks would all read exactly the same as the ground clocks opposite them — in other words they would all be in synchronism with each other and with the ground clocks.

It is interesting to realize that this assumption together with the assumption of the train clocks being out of synchronism when the train is moving, results in the consequence of a very irregular progress of the train clocks.

Thus, let us assume that at an instant i_a the train (Fig. 3-4) is stationary (in position P_a) with all the train clocks (and ground clocks) reading 0. Let us suppose that the train is started and that at some later instant i_b, when the train is in position P_b, it is moving with the velocity $\frac{1}{3}c$. According to the theory the train clocks must read differently, each reading later than the one in front of it (as shown in Fig. 3-2). If at instant i_b the clock at the origin of the train happens

23

to read 3 (position P_b) the train clocks at -3 and $+3$ in this case would read 4 and 2 as shown in Fig. 3-4.

Then if the train came to a stop when the clock at its origin read 6, the clocks at -3 and $+3$ would also read 6 according to the theory, as shown at position P_e.

Then if the train started backward and was moving with the velocity $c/3$ when the clock at the origin read 9 (position P_d) the other two train clocks would read 8 and 10 as shown.

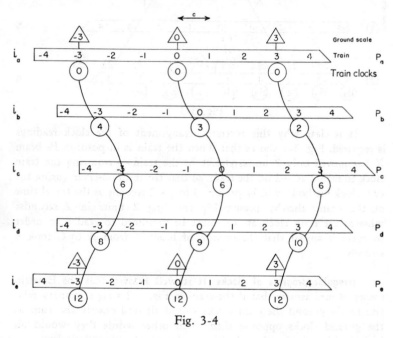

Fig. 3-4

Then if the train came to a stop when the clock at its origin read 12 (position P_e) the other two clocks would also read 12 according to the theory.

This means that during the first interval the train clock at -3 ran more rapidly than the clock at the origin whereas the clock at $+3$ ran more slowly than the clock at the origin; during the second and third intervals the rear clock ran more slowly than the middle clock and the front clock ran more rapidly than the middle clock. Then during the fourth interval the rear clock speeded up and the front clock slowed down.

Since all three clocks are subject to exactly the same motion of the train we would expect all three clocks to behave in the same way—

if the middle clock moved forward steadily we would expect the others to do the same. Einstein gives no explanation of this erratic behavior of the train clocks in accord with the Einstein theory.

An approximation. This illustration is to be regarded as approximate only because it disregards a slight contraction of the train which is presumed by the theory to take place when the train starts, as shown later (p. 34). However, this fact does not in any way invalidate the illustration as showing that, according to the theory, the same motion of a train causes clocks at different places on the train to behave differently — some to speed up and others to slow down. Indeed, a later and more rigorous illustration shows that according to the theory clocks must sometimes run backward. (See the heading: Clocks must run backward, p. 40).

Einstein's concept of time, requiring the arrangement of clock readings shown in Fig. 3-2, leads to a startling deduction. To understand this deduction let us examine Fig. 3-5, which is similar to Fig. 3-2, the difference being that the train is shown in positions representing ¾ second, 1 ½ second, etc., after instant 0, instead of 1 second, 2 seconds, and 3 seconds.

(If this figure were exactly in accord with the Einstein transformation equations, each train scale value and each train clock reading would be multiplied by a value k, explained later, but that would in no way effect the following reasoning.)

It will be seen that when the train is in position P_e the train clock at the origin (0 point) reads 8/3, showing that this train clock moves forward only 8/3 seconds while the ground clocks move forward 3, or 9/3 seconds. This makes it appear that according to the theory the train clocks in this case move forward only 8/9 as fast as the ground clocks. This is a forward motion of only ⅔ second from each train position to the next.

By interpolation we find that the train clock at −3 which reads 11/3 in position P_e, must read 9/3 or 3 when in position P_d as shown at D. And by extrapolation we find that the train clock at 1 must read 3 in position P_f (point F) and that the train clock at 3 must read 3 in position P_g (point G). That is, the train clocks at D, E, F, and G all read 3 according to the theory.

Thus we see that Einstein's concept of the train clocks reading differently in any given position of the train leads to the startling concept that

(1) the time on the train is 3 at −3 when the ground clocks read 2 ¼ ;

(2) the time on the train is 3 at −1 when the ground clocks read 3;

(3) the time on the train is 3 at +1 when the ground clocks read 3¾; and

(4) the time on the train is 3 at +3 when the ground clocks read 4½.

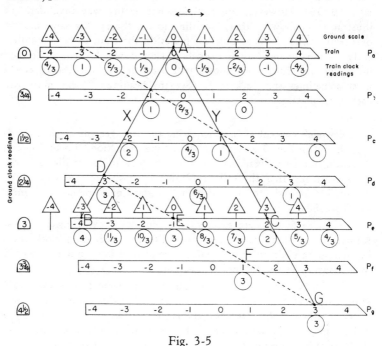

Fig. 3-5

The train clock reading 3 at point D is presumed to show, by the two-clock method, that beam X moved from the origin of the train to − 3 in 3 seconds by the train clocks. The train clock reading 3 at point G is presumed to show, by the two-clock method, that beam Y moved from the origin of the train to +3 in 3 seconds by the train clocks.

The sweep of time. Thus, according to the Einstein theory, when a train is in motion time sweeps forward over the train.*

Representing events. Point D in Fig. 3-5 may be considered to represent an event — the event of the train clock at −3 arriving at the

---

*It would be simple to show, in the light of Fig. 3-3, that if the train moves backward, time (a single instant by the train clocks) must be considered by the theory as sweeping over the train backward.

26

time 3. Let us call it event D. Similarly point E represents event E — the event of the train clock at -1 arriving at the time 3, etc.

Although events D, E. F and G occur in succession they are presumed by the theory to have the same clock reading (3). For this reason these events are regarded by the Einstein theory as occuring simultaneously on the train.

On the other hand, events B, E, and C are simultaneous but are assigned different train clock readings by the theory; and for this reason these events are regarded by the theory as occuring in succession on the train. These circumstances have led Einstein to say that events that are simultaneous on the ground are not simultaneous on a moving train, and vice versa.

Needless to say, a classicist cannot accept such an extraordinary concept.

Redefining simultaneity. Einstein would probably say that events D, E, F, and G are simultaneous on the train just as truly as events B, E, and C are simultaneous on the ground. If we asked him by what reasoning he presumed to call events D, E, F, and G simultaneous on the train, he would have to reply, in effect: Since the train clock readings of these events come out the same according to my theory, I merely declare that according to my theory these events are simultaneous on the train. I have simply redefined simultaneity on the train in accord with my theory. That is all.

Another viewpoint. We see that beam X in Fig. 3-5 took only $2\frac{1}{4}$ seconds to go from 0 to -3 along the train; whereas beam Y took $4\frac{1}{2}$ seconds to go from 0 to 3 along the train — equal distances relative to the train. We may say, therefore, that the essence of the Einstein theory in this case is merely to regard as 3 seconds on the train whatever time it takes a beam to travel 3 units along the train. That is a very simple way, of course, to make it appear that beams X and Y had the same velocity relative to the train as well as relative to the ground.

Scientists have found the velocity of light from a terrestriel source to be 300,000 km. per sec. relative to the earth. Stated more generally, therefore, we may say that the essence of the Einstein theory is merely to consider that *whatever time is required for a given beam to travel 300,000 km. in a given inertial system will be regarded as one second in that inertial system, as related to that particular beam.*

Attempt at rationalization. In the effort to rationalize the need for the clocks on a moving train to get out of synchronism according to the theory in a case such as that of Fig. 3-5, Einstein has tried to persuade his readers that events that are simultaneous on the ground are not simultaneous on a moving train (*Relativity*, p. 30). His argument is based upon an illustration substantially as follows:

Let trees A, B, and C be equidistant as in Fig. 3-6. Let beams X and Y be emitted *simultaneously* from trees A and B at instant i_o, arriving at tree C at instant i_1. Let a train be moving to the right past the row of trees. Let points A' and B' on the train coincide with trees A and B at instant i_o and let the mid-point M of the train coincide with tree C also at instant i_o.

Space-time lines A'F and B'D represent the motion of the beams, and space-time line MM represents the motion of the mid-point M of the train — at which an observer is riding.

It is clear from the graph that even though the beams were emitted simultaneously, beam Y will reach the observer at M on the train when the train is in the position P_a (prior to instant i_1) and that beam X will not reach the observer at M until instant i_b when the train is in position P_b.

We must take it for granted that any knowledgable persons, whether riding on the train or stationary on the ground, will understand that beams emitted simultaneously from trees A and B in this manner will arrive at the observer in succession, beam Y arriving first.

Now Einstein would have his reader believe that the observer on the train at M would be obliged to infer that the beams were not emitted simultaneously, merely because one reached him before the other! He bases his argument on the assumption that the observer on the train would be of necessity under the impression that the beams had equal velocities relative to the train as well as relative to the ground — as if he believed in the Einstein postulate of the 'constant velocity of light. But the reader is under no such impression.

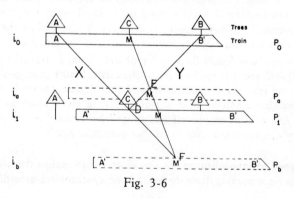

Fig. 3-6

Since the reader can see clearly from the figure that the beams can reach the observer in succession even though they were emitted simultaneously, he sees no reason for the observer on the train to infer otherwise. The argument is quite unconvincing!

To be sure, we can say that if the observer believes in the Einstein postulate he might be misled into inferring that the beams were not emitted simultaneously. But it was not necessary for Einstein to go to all this trouble to prove that according to his theory events that are simultaneous on the ground are not simultaneous on a moving train. That is obvious from Figures 3-5 and 4-1.

The constant-velocity postulate contradicted. On further thought, is it not clear that Einstein has contradicted his own postulate of the constant velocity of light when in effect he concedes that beam Y travels the distance MB' along the train in the short interval $i_o i_a$, whereas beam X requires the longer interval $i_o i_b$ to travel the equal distance $A'M$ along the train? Does this not indicate clearly that he admits that the beams had unequal velocities relative to the train?

A syllogism regarding simultaneity. Bergmann tells us (*Introduction to the Theory of Relativity*, p. 30) that in this connection if two events A and B are simultaneous, and events A and C are simultaneous, then events B and C are simultaneous.

Let A and B represent the departures of beams X and Y relative to the ground.

Let A' and B' represent the departures of beams X and Y relative to the train. Then events A and A' are simultaneous by identity; events B and B' are simultaneous by identity; and events A and B are simultaneous by stipulation. Hence according to Bergmann's syllogism events A' and B' are simultaneous — contradicting Einstein's assertion that these events are not simultaneous.

A panoramic photograph. It is interesting to realize that if it were possible to take a panoramic photograph of the train of Fig. 3-5 moving the slit so that the -3 mark of the train was photographed at instant $2\frac{1}{4}$ the -1 mark was photographed at instant 3, etc., with the 3 mark photographed at instant $4\frac{1}{2}$, we would have what would appear to be a stationary train with all the clocks on the train reading 3 and so making it appear that the photograph was an instantaneous one. If we could imagine the photograph showing the arrival of the beams at -3 and 3 of the train it would show that these events took place in both cases when the clocks at those places read 3. This would make it appear that the beams traveled equal distances (0 to —3 and 0 to 3) along the train both in 3 seconds, and hence at equal velocities.

We may say therefore that, in effect, Einstein's redefinition of simultaneity amounts to saying: I would consider the above-mentioned panoramic photograph as constituting an instantaneous photograph so far as the train is concerned.

Eternity becomes one instant. We must realize that in accord with with the Einstein theory there is no limit to the length of the line of Fig. 3-5 that connects the train clock readings of 3. That is, theoretically it extends to infinity in both directions, showing that the whole series of events of which events *D, E. F.* and *G* are mere samples, so to speak, extends from the infinite past to eternity in the future. Thus we may say that according to the Einstein theory under certain circumstances an infinite series of events may be considered as constituting a single instant.

An unacceptable concept. Referring to the Einstein concept of the 'relativity of simultaneity' according to which an infinite series of events must be regarded under certain circumstances as constituting a single instant, it hardly seems necessary to say that to the classicist this concept is so fantastic — so far from representing any reality — as to render the theory unacceptable without further consideration.

This concept appears to have had its origin when Lorentz found it convenient, mathematically, to use the symbol t' to denote a variable that he referred to casually as "local time", to distinguish it from his concept of "true time". The symbol t' acquired permanence in the Lorentz transformation equations, which were adopted by Einstein with a different interpretation as suitable for his purpose.

It is doubtful that Lorentz gave serious thought to the far-reaching implications of his 'local-time' concept. And, as we have seen, Einstein's attempt to justify the concept of the 'relativity of simultaneity' merely resulted in his showing that it was a consequence of his theory — which was already obvious from Fig. 3-5.

Summary. In section 3 it has been shown:

(1) that the Einstein theory is based upon three postulates: the relativity of motion, the uniformity of the laws of nature, and the constancy of the velocity of light.

(2) that the adoption of the postulate of the constant velocity of light appears to have been the result of mistaken reasoning;

(3) that the theory presumes to demonstrate the 'constant velocity of light' by merely assigning travel times to beams in proportion to the distance traveled;

(4) that the theory requires us to consider that the motion of a train can have different effects upon the clocks in different places on the train;

(5) that Einstein is obliged to redefine simultaneity on a moving train so that an infinite series of events will be regarded as a single instant on the train — a concept that the classicist considers to be so untenable as to render the theory unacceptable.

(6) that Einstein's argument by which he attempts to rationalize his concept of the relativity of simultaneity (by means of the train and embankment illustration) is unconvincing.

4. THE TRANSFORMATION EQUATIONS

The Simple Method in accord with the Einstein theory. We have been discussing a Simple Method of demonstrating the constancy of the velocity of light which we have said represents the essence of the Einstein theory. For the reader who is familiar with the mathematics of the Einstein theory it may be well, therefore, to show at this point that what has been said about the lack of synchronism of train clocks, the use of the two-clock method, the erratic behavior of clocks on an accelerating train, etc. is strictly in accord with the Einstein theory.

The transformation equations of the Einstein theory. The mathematics of the Einstein theory are based upon two fundamental 'transformation equations',

$$x' = k(x - vt) \tag{1}$$

and

$$t' = k(t - vx/c^2) \tag{2}$$

in which in the case of Fig. 3-2 for example,

x = the ground scale reading of any given point P,

x' = the train scale reading at that point,

t = the ground clock reading at point P,

t' = the train clock reading at that point;

v = the velocity of the train (which in Fig. 3-2 is 1 unit in 3 seconds or $\frac{1}{3}$ unit per second.)

c = the velocity of light relative to the ground (which in Fig. 3-2 is 3 units in 3 seconds or 1 unit per second); and

k = $1/\sqrt{(1 - v^2/c^2)}$.

Fig. 4-1 shows the exact train scale readings and train clock readings that would be assigned to the train of Fig. 3-5 in accord with the Einstein transformation equations (eqs. 1 and 2 above).

Obtaining the train scale and train clock readings. Before discussing Fig. 4-1 let us see how the train scale and train clock readings in that figure were obtained by means of the Einstein transformation equations (1) and (2).

In the case of point H, for example, the value of x (the ground scale reading) is $2\frac{1}{2}$. The value of t (the ground clock reading) is $1\frac{1}{2}$.

In this figure v is $\frac{1}{3}$ unit per second, and c is 1 unit per second. Hence for point H,

x' (the train scale reading) = $k(x - v \times t)$
$$= k[2\frac{1}{2} - (\frac{1}{3} \times 1\frac{1}{2})] = 2k$$

and t' (the train clock reading) = $k[t - v \times x/c^2]$
$$= k[1\frac{1}{2} - (\frac{1}{3} \times 2\frac{1}{2})/1^2] = \frac{2}{3}k,$$

the value shown in the circle.

Similar computations would show that all the train scale readings and train clock readings in Fig. 4-1 are derived from and in accord with the Einstein transformation equations.

The value of k. No use need be made of the value of k in this discussion, but it may be explained that in this case, in which $v/c = \frac{1}{3}$ the value of k is $\sqrt{(9/8)}$. That is, $k = 1/\sqrt{(1-v^2/c^2)} = 1/\sqrt{(1-1/9} = 1/\sqrt{(8/9)} = \sqrt{(9/8)}$. The value of k is always greater than 1. It becomes infinity when $v = c$.

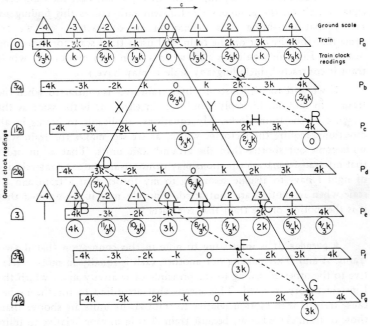

Fig. 4-1

It will be seen that Fig. 4-1 is the same as Fig. 3-5 except that each train scale reading and train clock reading in Fig. 3-5 has been multiplied by the factor k in Fig. 4-1.

The need for the factor k. The reader may wonder why the factor k is required in the Einstein transformation equations. Briefly stated, one reason is that Einstein found the introduction of the factor k into the transformation equations to be necessary in order to obtain from them values of train scale readings and train clock readings, for example, such that beams emitted *in any direction* from a source on the ground

33

would appear to have velocities equal relative to a moving train — not merely beams projected forward and backward along the train.

The use of the factor k is exemplified on p. 46 and p. 48.

Contraction of the moving train scale. It may be seen from Fig. 4-1 that according to the Einstein theory, when the train is in position P_0, for example, the train scale readings are presumed to be not —4, —3, —2, etc., as in Fig. 3-5, but —4k, —3k, —2k, etc.

This means that according to the theory k units on the train scale equal 1 unit on the ground scale. Einstein rationalizes this finding by saying that measuring rods in motion are contracted. (If we assume that the observer on the train will use a train scale for measuring distances, Einstein would say that when a train is in motion the whole train is contracted, including any scale it may have.)

If we were to ask Einstein why a train scale is contracted when the train is in motion, his reply would be, in effect: It is the same as the slowing of the train clocks. My equations, applicable to beams in all directions, require the factor k, which, as we see, makes the train scale units come out shorter than the ground scale units. That is, in order that my transformation equations may demonstrate the constant velocity of light I have to assume according to my theory that a train and its scale when in motion are contracted. I merely take it for granted that it is the motion of the train that contracts it.

A paradox. It is interesting to note in this connection that if two trains, A and B are passing one another, each is equally in motion relative to the other according to the principle of relativity upon which the Einstein theory is based. This means that according to the theory because train B is in motion relative to train A, its units are shorter than those of train A: whereas, because train A is in motion relative to train B, its units are shorter than those of train B. This is one of the 'paradoxes' of the theory.

Modified train clock readings. As mentioned above, each train clock reading in Fig. 3-5 has been multiplied by k in Fig. 4-1. We see however, that in accord with the scale and clock readings of Fig. 4-1, it is presumed by the theory that an observer on the train, using the two-clock method of timing, will find that beam X traveled 4k units in 4k seconds, which is 1 unit per second; and will find that beam Y traveled 2k units in 2k seconds, which is also 1 unit per second — making the velocities of the beams appear to be equal relative to the train.

Characteristics of the Einstein theory. We see that Fig. 4-1 shows the same lack of synchronism of the train clocks as in Fig. 3-5; it shows the same need for the two-clock method of timing to obtain 'travel times' required to make it appear that the velocities of beams X and Y are equal relative to the train; it shows the same sweep of time, the same redefinition of simultaneity, etc. All these are shown, therefore, to be characteristics of the Einstein theory.

Effect of change of velocity on clock readings. It is interesting to note that according to the Einstein theory the greater is the velocity v of the train relative to the ground, the farther are the train clocks out of synchronism. Thus, let us suppose the velocity v of the train of Fig. 4-1 to be not $\frac{1}{3} c$ but $\frac{2}{3} c$. Then let us compute from the transformation equation t' (train clock reading) $= k (t - vx/c^2)$ the train clock readings (t') corresponding to the values 1, 2, 3, and 4 of x (the ground scale readings). Let us find these clock readings for the ground time $t = 3$, at which the train clock readings in Fig. 4-1 were $4k$, $11/3 \ k$, $10/3 \ k$, etc., (beginning at the left).

For our new purpose we are to let $c = 1$ (as before), $v = \frac{2}{3}$ (new value) and $t = 3$ (as before). Hence by the equation $t' = k \ (t - vx/c^2)$ we find that

when $x = 0$, $\quad t' = k (3 - 0) = 3k$ or $9/3 \ k$;
when $x = 1$, $\quad t' = k (3 - \frac{2}{3}) = 7/3 \ k$;
when $x = 2$, $\quad t' = k (3 - 4/3) = 5/3 \ k$; etc.

This means that when $v = \frac{2}{3} \ c$ instead of $\frac{1}{3} \ c$, the train clock readings at trees, 0, 1, 2, 3, and 4 are not
$9/3 \ k$, $8/3 \ k$, $7/3 \ k$, $6/3 \ k$, and $5/3 \ k$ — as in Fig. 4-1, but
$9/3 \ k$, $7/3 \ k$, $5/3 \ k$, $3/3 \ k$, and $1/3 \ k$ — showing that in this case the train clocks are, as we might say, twice as far out of synchronism as in Fig. 4-1.

When v = c. It is interesting to learn that if the train of Fig. 4-1 could suddenly acquire the velocity c relative to the ground at the time $t = 1$ (when the train clock at tree 0 read k) the following would happen according to the theory:

1. The train would suddenly have its length contracted to zero and consist of a mere plane at tree 0 perpendicular to the line of motion and having merely the extent of the cross section of the train.

2. The train clocks would cease to run altogether, or (since the clocks would be crumpled flat) we might say that train time would remain k and never get any later.

3. If there could be any clocks in the inertial system of the train, other than at the train, those behind the train would all read plus infinity and those ahead of the train would read minus infinity.

It is for this reason that Einstein says that according to his theory no object can have a velocity as great as c. (He means relative to any inertial system.)

Slowing of clocks in a 'moving system'. The reason Einstein is required by his theory to assume that the clocks on the train in Fig. 3-5 run more slowly than those on the ground can be understood more clearly, perhaps, by an examination of Fig. 4-2 which is a simplification and extension of Fig. 3-5. (For simplicity the factor k is disregarded.)

In both Figs. 3-5 and 4-2 the arrivals of the beams at trees — 3 and 3 are represented by events B and C and the arrivals of the beams at the —3 and 3 marks of the train are represented by events D and G.

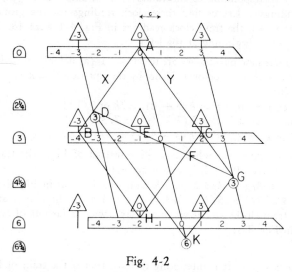

Fig. 4-2

If the beams are reflected by stationary mirrors at trees —3 and 3, they will follow the 'paths' BH and CH, uniting at tree 0 at instant 2 (event H). But if they are reflected by stationary mirrors at D and G they will follow the 'paths' DK and GK and will unite at the 0 point of the train but *not until a later instant* (event K).

The reason it takes beam X longer to travel 3 units two ways along the train is that it travels 'path' AD for only 2¼ seconds; whereas it takes 4½ seconds to travel 'path' DK; that is, it travels slowly *longer* than it travels rapidly, relative to the train.

36

And it is for a corresponding reason that it takes longer for beam Y to travel the 6 units of 'path' ADK along the train than to travel the 6 units of 'path' ABH along the ground.

It is easy to demonstrate in this manner that the faster the train goes the greater is the time required for a beam from a source on the ground to travel 3 units and back along the train. That is, the faster the train goes, the more slowly its clocks must run according to the theory.

Different redefinitions of simultaneity. It was explained in connection with Fig. 3-5 how Einstein is obliged to redefine simultaneity on the

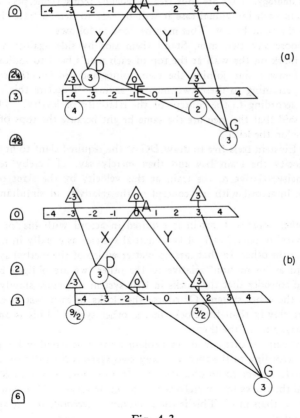

Fig. 4-3

37

train when it is in motion. The need to redefine simultaneity relative to the train differently for each different velocity of the train is made clear by a comparison of graphs (*a*) and (*b*) of Fig. 4-3. Graph (*a*) is merely the top portion of Fig. 4-2 in which $v = \frac{1}{3} c$. (The factor k of the theory is disregarded for simplicity.) Graph (*b*) shows the train moving with the greater velocity $v = \frac{1}{2} c$.

In each case simultaneity relative to the train is represented by the slant of the line *DG* and redefined accordingly. (In each case *D* and *G* are the events of the arrival of beams *X* and *Y* at −3 and 3 of the train scale, as in Fig. 4-2.

We see that the line *DG* has a steeper slant in graph (*b*) than in graph (*a*). This shows that different definitions of simultaneity are needed for the train when it has different velocities.

An analogy. If we are thus free to redefine terms (concepts) differently to fit each individual case it will be easy to demonstrate that all men are the same height. This may be done as follows.

Choose any two men. Stand them side by side against a wall. Make a mark on the wall at the top of each man's head to indicate his height. Draw a line joining the two points and *redefine the concept level* as pertaining to these two men by saying. "I declare this line to be level according to the concept of the relativity of levelty." Then it may be said that the men are the same height because the tops of their heads are 'on the level'.

So Einstein feels free to draw *DG* of the required slant to fit whatever velocity the train has and then merely say, "I hereby redefine simultaneity relative to the train at this velocity by the slant of this line *DG*, in accord with my concept of the relativity of simultaneity."

Another paradox. Einstein is required in accord with his 'principle of relativity' to regard each of two inertial systems as equally in motion relative to the other. In that case no matter which of the inertial systems we regard as 'in motion' relative to the other, we are obliged by the theory to consider that the clocks in that system run more slowly than those in the other system. Of course the clocks in each system cannot run more slowly than the clocks in the other system. This is another of the paradoxes of the theory.

The attempt is often made to explain away this paradox by asserting that according to the theory in any two systems *S* and *S'* the clocks in *S'* merely *appear to an observer in S* to run more slowly in *S'* than in *S*; and the clocks in *S* merely appear to an observer in *S'* to run more slowly in *S* than in *S'*. This is the *appearance interpretation* as applied to clock rates.

Slower running of clocks actual according to the theory. The discussion of Fig. 4-2 should make it clear, however, that in order to maintain that beams X and Y have equal velocities of 3 units per second relative to the train as well as relative to the ground (that is, by the train clocks as well as by the ground clocks) Einstein is obliged to consider that according to his theory the train clocks in this case *actually* run more slowly than the ground clocks; and that in any inertial system S' that is 'in motion' relative to a system S, the clocks in S' *actually* run more slowly than those in S. And yet the clocks in system S, which is 'in motion' relative to system S', must *actually* run more slowly than those in system S'.

An impossible consequence. Thus we see that the apperance interpretation fails to explain away the fact that the theory requires that in two systems the clocks in each run more slowly than those in the other. To the classicist this impossibility invalidates the theory.

Section 5 points out other contradictions in the theory.

An attempt to explain away the paradox. It is interesting to note that often an Einsteinist presumes to explain away the clock paradox by saying merely that there is not complete symmetry between two clocks (or two twins) that are each in motion relative to the other. He merely cites the fact that if the clocks were at one time togther one must have been subject to an acceleration to give it motion relative to the other. It is then deemed permissible to say that accordiag to the Einstein theory the clock that has been under acceleration is the one that runs more slowly than the other and there is no longer any paradox.

This explanation fails to remove the paradox for two reasons.

First, the special theory of relativity, in stating that "a clock in motion runs more slowly than one at rest" says nothing at all about any acceleration. Hence the argument merely brings in an entirely extraneous concept that has nothing to do with the special theory.

Secondly, suppose the clocks are initially together and that the two clocks are then accelerated equally in opposite directions. There is then complete symetry. Which clock will the Einsteinist then claim is the one that runs more slowly than the other?

If he says they run at equal rates he repudiates Einstein's concept that when a clock is in motion relative to another clock it runs more slowly than the other clock.

Another attempt to explain away the paradox. Einsteinists often attempt to explain away the paradox by saying that if observer A (on train A) and observer B (on train B) each observe the other's clock he will find it running more slowly than his own clock — in accord with the principle of relativity.

Let us say that at a moment when the trains are together the observers compare their watches and find them indicating the same time. Let us say the trains recede from one another for an extended time and then return to the starting point. The above 'explanation' would mean that if each observer could have kept a telescope trained on the other's watch he would have found it running more slowly than his throughout the motion of the trains. If the watches read the same at the start and one ran more slowly than the other during the motion of the trains, it would read earlier than the other when the trains came together.

Now let us say that the observers are back together. Observer A has been seeing observer B's watch run more slowly than his own and observer B has been seeing observer A's watch run more slowly than his.

The above attempt to explain away the paradox amounts, therefore, to saying that even as observers A and B stand side by side each observing both watches, each will find his own watch reading earlier than the other's watch! Two men seeing two watches and disagreeing as to which reads earlier than the other!

Will the reader be content with this attempt to explain how each of two clocks in relative motion can run more slowly than the other in accord with the theory?

The true explanation of the paradox. To those who may be interested, it is possible to show that actually according to the equations of the theory, motion as such does not slow a clock. Hence the basis of the paradox is itself fictitious. On careful analysis we find that according to one definition of simultaneity one of two clocks does run more slowly than the other; whereas, according to another definition of simultaneity the second clock does run more slowly than the first. If one can accept the Einstein concept of the 'relativity of simultaneity' there is no paradox. Hence the attempts of Einsteinists to explain away the paradox in the ways described are all idle and to no purpose.

Clocks must run backward. It was stated earlier that according to the theory under certain circumstances clocks must run backward. This fact can be shown rigorously as follows.

For convenience let us use the equation $t' = t/k - vx'/c^2$, which is derivable from the transformation equations (1) and (2).

We know that according to the theory when a train is at rest all its clocks read the same. Let us suppose a train to start from rest at the

40

instant the ground clocks read 0 and at which the train clocks also read 0. Let us say that the train very quickly attains a velocity of $\frac{2}{3}$ c, when the train has that velocity the value of k (that is, $1/\sqrt{(1 - v^2/c^2)} = 1/\sqrt{(1 - 4/9)} = 1.34$, which let us call $4/3$.

Let us now find the train clock reading (t') at several scale points along the train at the instant $t = 4/3$ (so that $t/k = 1$). Let $c = 1$.

When $x' = 0$, $t' = t/k - vx'/c^2) = 1 - 0 = 1$.
When $x' = 3$, $t' = 1 - 6/3 = -1$.
When $x' = 6$, $t' = 1 - 4 = -3$
When $x' = 9$, $t' = 1 - 6 = -5$ etc.

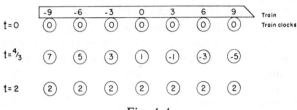

Fig. 4-4

These clock readings are shown in the second row of circles in Fig. 4-4.

It can be shown that at any moment any train clock that happens to be midway between the origins of the train and ground scales will read the same as the ground clocks. Let us say the train comes to a sudden stop just as the train clock midway between the origins reads 2. At this instant, at which $t = 2$ also, we would expect all the other train clocks to read 2 also, as shown in the third row of circles.

Theoretically there is no limit to the extent of an inertial system; hence theoretically the clock readings shown in the second row of circles may be regarded as extending from minus infinity to plus infinity.

It is clear from the figure that the train clocks at 3, 6, and 9, which read 0 when $t = 0$ and read -1, -3, and -5 when $t = 4/3$ must have run backward at some time during the interval. And similarily the train clocks at -3, -6, and -9, must have run backward at some time after reading 3, 5, and 7 in order to read 2 when $t = 2$.

That the acceleration or deceleration of a train could cause certain of its clocks to run backward is regarded by the classicist as unrealistic.

An unacceptable concept. Actually, according to the Einstein theory, whatever a clock does, so does time; that is, if a train clock slows down, time itself slows down at that point; if a train clock runs backward, time itself runs backward at that point. In the case of Fig. 4-4 this

41

would mean that at point 9 on the train time ran backward then forward; whereas at point —9 time ran forward then backward.

The classicist regards the concept of time running backward as wholly outside the realm of reality and hence rendering the theory unacceptable.

Reversed sequence. Let the reader consider this question? Would you accept as valid any theory according to which two events A and B could occur in the order A-B on the ground and in the order B-A on a moving train?

It is interesting to realize that such a reversal of sequence is one of the consequences of the Einstein theory.

For example, let us consider an event J occuring at the $4k$ mark of the train of Fig. 4-1 at instant $\frac{3}{4}$. Let us compare this event with event A, the event of the coinciding of the origin of the train scale with tree 0. Event J occurred after event A by ground time ($\frac{3}{4}$ is later than 0); whereas event J occurred *before* event A according to the alleged train time. Calculating by transformation equation (2) would show the train clock reading for event J to be $-\frac{2}{3}$ k which is before the time 0.

Thus we see that according to the theory it is possible for events A and B to occur in the order $A - B$ in one inertial system and in the order $B - A$ in another inertial system.

Indeed, theoretically, we could draw a line through points A and J in Fig. 4-1 and consider it as extending indefinitely in each direction. Every point on this line would represent an event. Let us assume that as we move to the right along this line we find after J the points K, L, M, N, etc., in order. These points represents events that occur in the order K, L, M, N, etc., relative to the ground but which occur in the order N, M, L, K, etc., relative to the train — according to the theory. And correspondingly for points to the left of A.

Thus we see that according to the theory it is possible for an infinite series of events (represented by points on the line AJ of infinite length) to occur in one order relative to the ground and in the reverse order relative to the train.

The classicist can find nothing about the theory more unthinkable than that.

Do clocks have intelligence? The following discussion is intended to show that according to the Einstein theory clocks seem to be endowed with intelligence.

In Fig. 4-5 the upper drawing in both graphs (a) and (b) shows a train stationary at instant 0 opposite a row of trees A, B, C, D, E, and

F. Each graph represents the train as starting to move from rest at instant 0 by the ground clocks at which according to the theory all the clocks on the train also read 0.

In each graph the second drawing represents the train at instant 1, one second later by ground time at which instant the train is supposed to be moving with the velocity of ⅓ *c* and to have arrived at position ⅓ *c* to the right of its original position (as if it had attained the velocity ⅓ *c* instantly after starting).

We know that the choice of the origin of the scale in any inertial system is entirely arbitrary. Hence in graph (a) we have chosen to let tree *B* constitute the origin of the ground scale.

The graph shows that according to the transformation equations of the theory the train clock readings at instant 1 will be such that the clock opposite tree *B* reads *k*, the other clocks reading as shown, in accord with Fig. 4-1.

It is interesting to note, however, that if we had chosen to let tree *E* be the origin of the ground scale, as shown in graph (b), then at instant 1 the train clock opposite tree *E* would be the one to read *k*, the train clock opposite tree *B* reading 12/9 *k* instead of k.

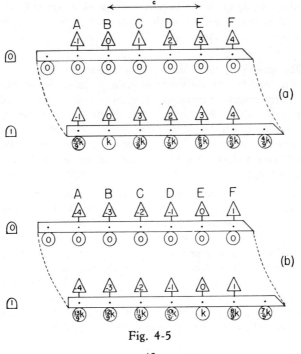

Fig. 4-5

43

This raises an interesting question. How do the train clocks, which all read 0 at instant 0, know which tree we have chosen to represent the origin of the ground scale; that is, how does the train clock opposite tree B at the start know whether to reach the reading k or the reading $12/9\ k$ by instant 1? And similarly for the other train clocks.

It might be argued, perhaps, that in the above illustration the behavior of the train clocks would depend upon where the origin of the train scale was; that is, that if it coincided with the origin of the ground scale at tree B, the clocks would behave as in graph (a); whereas, if it coincided with the origin of the ground scale at tree E, the clocks would behave is in graph (b).

The question would then arise: How do the train clocks know what point of the train scale has been chosen to be its origin?

It would seem that in accord with the theory we are obliged to endow the train clocks with a modicum of intelligence!

Needless to say, the classicist cannot accept a theory that has such a requirement. This illustration is sufficient to convince the classicist that the theory is essentially a mathematical theory according to which if, in any particular case, clocks behave in an arbitrary way to fit that particular case, and if it can be assumed that observers will time beams by the unrealistic two-clock method, then the velocity of a beam will always come out the same.

The slowing of time. We have seen that the Einstein theory is obliged to consider that on a moving train clocks run more slowly than clocks on the grund: or more generally, any clock 'in motion' runs more slowly than it does when 'at rest'. But Einstein goes further and states that according to his theory time itself on the train flows more slowly than time on the ground. This appears to be according to the concept that whatever a clock does, so does time where the clock is. Is this a rational concept?

Let us say we have a pendulum clock that ticks off exact seconds at sea level. Let us say we are able to take it to the top of a mountain sufficiently high that, because of the reduced force of gravity, the clock runs only half as fast as it did at sea level. Would we say that time at the top of the mountain flowed only half as fast as at sea level? If our clock registered 12 o'clock at noon at the top of the mountain we might find the sun setting at 3 P.M. by the clock. Would we decide that where we were the sun really set at 3 P.M.? Would we not consider that time flowed on at the same rate at the top of the mountain as at sea level regardless of the varying of clock rates at different altitudes?

44

Why then, must we accept Einstein's concept that whatever happens to clock rates also happens to the rate of flow of time itself?

Slowing of body processes. Einstein goes even further and states that if a man were to travel on a space ship at a high speed such that according to his theory a clock on the space ship ran only $1/10$ as fast, let us say, as when on the earth, the body processes of the man would proceed also at only $1/10$ the normal rate so that in 10 years of such travel the man would 'age' only one year. In accord with this concept, if the space ship could attain the speed of light relative to the earth, time on the space ship would cease to flow and the man would cease to age so that he could live forever if the space ship could keep going at that rate.

Einstein gives no reason for such dependence of the rate of bodily processes upon the rate of flow of time and indeed upon the rate of clocks. It would seem to the classicist that the man at the top of the mountain, whose clock indicated a two-minute interval as only one minute, would find his heart beating twice as fast as normal—by the clock.

Einstein's concept of the flow of time being dependent upon the rate of a clock and the rate of body processes being dependent upon the rate of flow of time appears to the classicist as being pure fantacy and in in no sense in accord with reality.

If this concept is not in accord with reality is it not time to cease talking seriously about space travel without aging?

Time in proportion to distance. It was stated on page 33 that the factor k was required in the Einstein transformation equations in order that according to these equations beams emitted from a source on the ground in any direction (as well as forward and backward along the train) would have equal calculated velocities relative to the train.

It was indicated also (p. 22) that the Einstein transformation equations constitute a mathematical device for assigning to the travel of any two or more beams in any inertial system travel times exactly in proportion to the calculated distances traveled by the beams.

These facts are illustrated in Fig. 4-6 in which five beams, A, B, C. D, and E, are represented as emitted from a point O which we may think of as the origin of a system S, the beams being emitted in system S in the direction OA, OB, OC, OD, and OE. It is supposed that a system S' moves to the right relative to system S, that its origin O' coincided with origin O of system S at the instant (instant i_0) at which the five beams were emitted, and that the velocity v of system S' relative to system S is $\frac{1}{3}$ c. The semicircle represents the position of the wave front (of which the beams are elements) at instant i_1, i.e., after

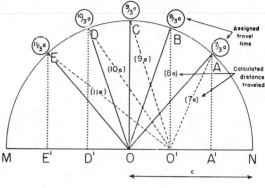

Fig. 4-6

1 second of travel in system S. At this instant $(t = 1)$ the origin of system S' is shown as having moved $\frac{1}{3}$ c from point O to point O' in the figure.

It can be shown that the distance beam A has traveled during the second relative to system S' is represented by the line $O'A$, the distance beam B has traveled relative to S' is represented by line $O'B$, etc.

Letting the distance ON represent c and letting the distance OO' be regarded for convenience as one unit in system S, it follows that OA, OB, etc. are 3 units long. Line MN is divided into 6 equal parts, each 1 unit long in system S but k units long in system S', according to the transformation equations.

Calculating velocities in system S'. In order to calculate the velocities the beams are presumed by the theory to have in system S' we must calculate the distances $O'A$, $O'B$, etc. which have been traveled by the beams in system S' according to the theory; then calculate the travel times of the beams according to the theory; and then obtain the velocities from these distances and travel times.

To find distance $O'A$ presumed by the theory to have been traveled by beam A in system S' we must first find $A'A$ from OA and OA'. In system S, $OA = 3$ and $OA' = 2$; hence $AA' = \sqrt{(3^2 - 2^2)} = \sqrt{5}$. This line is presumed by the theory to be the same length in system S' as in system S. Now with $O'A'$ equaling k in system S' the theory assumes that $O'A$ as measured in system $S' = \sqrt{(k^2 + 5)}$. And in this case in which $v/c = \frac{1}{3}$, $k = 1/\sqrt{(1 - 1/9)} = \sqrt{(9/8)}$. Hence $k^2 = 9/8$. So $O'A'$, as measured in S' is assumed to be $\sqrt{(9/8 + 5)}$, or $\sqrt{(49/8)}$, or $7\sqrt{(1/8)}$.

46

To find the travel time assigned by the theory to this beam we use the transformation equation $t' = k(t - vx/c^2)$; that is, equation (2), p. 32. We have let $v = 1$ and in the case of beam A, $x = 2$; hence by the equation, $t' = k(1 - 2/9) = 7/9 \, k = 7/9 \times \sqrt{(9/8)} = 7/3 \times \sqrt{(1/8)}$. For convenience let $\sqrt{(1/8)}$ be represented by a. Then $O'A$, as measured in $S' = 7a$ and the travel time is $7/3 \, a$, according to the theory.

In the case of beam B, the distance $O'B = \sqrt{(3^2 - 1^2)} = \sqrt{8} = 8\sqrt{(1/8)} = 8a$. This distance is presumed by the theory to be measured the same in both systems. According to the theory the time of travel of beam B in S' is $t' = k(t - vx/c^2) = k(1 - 1/9) = 8/9 \, k = 8/9 \times \sqrt{(9/8)} = 8/3 \times \sqrt{(1/8)} = 8/3 \, a$.

In this manner the distances traveled by the beams in system S' and the S' travel times presumed by the theory have been calculated. These are shown in the following table and in Fig. 4-6.

Beam	A	B	C	D	E
Distance traveled in S'	$7a$	$8a$	$9a$	$10a$	$11a$
Travel time in S'	$7a/3$	$8a/3$	$9a/3$	$10a/3$	$11a/3$

Thus we see that the transformation equations make the alleged travel times in system S' *come out exactly in proportion* to the calculated distances traveled — so as to make the velocities of the beams in system S' come out the same (3 units per second in this case).

Einstein would say: Certainly the transformation equations do just that. They were devised for precisely that purpose.

An interesting observation. Let us say that at an instant i_0 a beam of light is emitted at a point A and moves to the right in a system S with velocity c, and that an observer passing point A at instant i_0 also moves to the right with velocity c — so that the observer and beam are traveling side by side.

It is interesting to realize that we would be obliged by the Einstein theory to assume that the observer would find the beam moving away from him with the velocity c. (According to the postulate of the 'constant velocity of light' any observer will find the velocity of any beam relative to him to be c.) Let us see how the theory demonstrates this.

The observer is presumed to be carrying a clock with him with which to measure the time of travel of the beam. According to the theory, when a clock moves with velocity v its rate is reduced to the fraction $\sqrt{(1 - v^2/c^2)}$ of the rate it had when stationary. Now in this case, by stipulation, the velocity v of the observer and his clock is also c. Hence, according to the theory, the rate of the observer's clock is reduced to $\sqrt{(1 - c^2/c^2)}$ which, of course, is 0. That is, according to the theory the observer's clock in this case is stopped altogether. Hence it will show no elapsed time from instant i_0 to instant i_1 — a one-second interval by the clock in system S.

Now since the observer and beam are moving side by side the observer will find the beam to move the distance 0 from him during the interval. But to find the velocity of the beam relative to him he is required by the theory to divide the observed distance traveled during the interval by the time taken by his clock — that is, to divide the distance 0 by the time 0. This is presumed to yield the velocity c. To be sure, 0/0 can equal c or anything else, as any mathematician knows. Hence Einstein considers it reasonable to say that according to his theory a beam that is moving in coincidence with an observer may be regarded by the observer as moving away from him with the velocity $c!$

Aberration as interpreted by the theory. As indicated above (p. 9), the Einstein theory presumes to explain away the difference in velocity of a beam relative to the cosmos and relative to a moving telescope by assigning different travel times to the two paths. This is done in accord with the transformation equations of the theory, as follows.

In Fig. 4-7 line AB represents the verticle path of a beam relative to the cosmos. We suppose a telescope to move horizontally to the right, tilted so that the star may be seen through it as it moves.

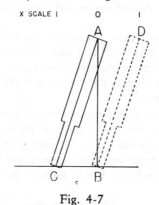

Fig. 4-7

Let us assume for convenience that the angle of the telescope in the figure is such that $CB = \frac{1}{3}$ of AB. This would mean that in this case $v/c = \frac{1}{3}$. Hence the value of k in the transformation equations applying to this case would be $k = 1/\sqrt{(1 - v^2/c^2)} = 1/\sqrt{(1 - 1/9)} = 1/\sqrt{(8/9)} = \sqrt{(9/8)}$.

48

For convenience let x and t represent scale and clock readings in the cosmos which we may call system S, and let x' and t' represent the corresponding measures relative to the telescope or observatory, which let us call system S'. Let us consider event A as occurring at the instant of the coinciding origins of the two systems (instant 0). Let us assume the telescope to be in the position AC when $t = 0$ and in the position BD when $t = 3$. Event B then occurs when $t = 3$. Let us call this instant 3. For convenience let $CB = c$; then $AB = 3c$.

We have now to find the time interval during which the beam traveled down the centerline of the telescope as measured in system S', according to the theory.

To do so we are to find the value of t' — the telescope clock reading for event B when the telescope is in the position BD; that is, when $t = 3$ and $x = 0$. According to the theory, for event B, $t' = k(t - vx/c^2) = k(3 - 0) = 3k$. Considering that t' for event A is 0, the theory presumes that the beam took $3k$ seconds by telescope time to travel down the telescope, even though it took only 3 seconds to traverse the path AB relative to the cosmos, and even though the beam traversed both paths with the *same motion,* and hence in the *same interval.*

In this case the theorem of Pythagoras would give the length of CA as $\sqrt{(3^2 + 1^2)}$ units $= \sqrt{(10)}$ units (unit $= c$) but according to the transformation equations the theory presumes that as measured in system S' (telescope) the distance CA will be slightly greater than $\sqrt{(10)}$ because CB will be measured as k units instead of 1 unit. This is so because $x' = k(x - vt) = k(0 - \frac{1}{3}$ of 3$) = -k$ units.)

Hence according to the theory, CA, as measured in system S', $= \sqrt{(3^2 + k^2)} = \sqrt{(9 + 9/8)} = \sqrt{(72/8 + 9/8)} = \sqrt{(81/8)} = 3\sqrt{(9/8)} = 3k$ units. (The measure $3\sqrt{(9/8)}$ is slightly greater than $\sqrt{10}$.)

What the transformation equations do in this case, therefore, is to assign the value $3k$ to the distance CA (as it is presumed to be measured in system S') instead of the slightly lesser measure $\sqrt{(10)}$ obtained by the theorem of Pythagoras; and to assign a travel time of $3k$ seconds to the travel of the beam down the telescope, even though the time is only 3 seconds in system S. Then according to the theory the velocity of the beam down the telescope will be computed to be $3k$ units in $3k$ seconds, or 1 unit per second the same as in system S.

If we apply the equation $t' = k(t - vx/c^2)$ we find that at instant 0 when the telescope is in the position CA ($t = 0$) the telescope clock at A reads 0 and the telescope clock at C reads $\frac{1}{3} k$; and that at instant 3 when the telescope is in the position BD ($t = 3$) the telescope clock at B reads $3k$ and the telescope at D reads $2\frac{2}{3}\ k$. To the classicist this means that in each of these positions the two clocks of the telescope are out of synchronism (read differently).

Einstein explains the different telescope readings in position CA by saying merely that by telescope time the lower end of the telescope arrived at the position CA $\frac{1}{3}\ k$ second *after* the upper end arrived in that position!

Use of the two-clock method of timing. We have seen that in order to make the velocity of the beam down the telescope come out the same as its velocity down the vertical path it is necessary to assume that the observer at the telescope will obtain the travel time $3k$ seconds for the passage of the beam down the telescope. In order that this assumption may be made the theory requires us to assume that the observer will time the entry of the beam into the telescope by the clock at the top of the telescope which reads 0 at instant 0 but will time the arrival of the beam at the bottom of the telescope by the clock at the bottom of the telescope, which reads $3k$ at instant 3, even though the two clocks on the telescope are out of synchronism in the sense that they read differently both at instant 0 and at instant 3. The classicist asserts that it is unreasonable to assume that any observer would use such a two-clock method of timing.

Using the same clock. If either clock were used to time both the beginning and end of the motion of the beam down the telescope the time interval would come out only $8/3\ k$ seconds ($3k - \frac{1}{3}\ k$ by the lower clock and $8/3\ k - 0$ by the upper clock). Then the velocity of the beam down the telescope would have to be calculated as $3k$ units in $8/3\ k$ seconds and so would not come out 1 unit per second as in the case of the vertical path in the cosmos.

A fictitious comparison. The classicist regards it as quite unnecessary and fictitious to assume the existence of a hypothetical observer at rest in the cosmos who would obtain 3 seconds as the time of the motion of the beam down the vertical path and with whose computation that of the observer at the telescope would be compared. The classicist asserts that even if the astronomer at the telescope went to the trouble of timing the beginning and end of the motion of the beam down the telescope he would know that these clock readings sufficed also for timing the beginning and end of the motion down the vertical path because the beam began both motions at the same instant and ended both motions at the same instant. Knowing that the paths had different lengths,

50

he could deduce for himself that the velocities down the two paths were different.

Summary of Section 4. In this section it has been shown:—

(1) that the Einstein theory is essentially a mathematical theory based upon two fundamental 'transformation equations' by means of which the theory assigns scale readings and clock readings in a 'moving' system S' which are different from those that would be obtained in a 'stationary' system S, and in accord with which the velocity of a given beam will come out the same in system S' as in system S;

(2) that Einstein's statement that measuring rods in motion are contracted, considered in the light of his 'principle of relativity', according to which each of two inertial systems is equally in motion relative to the other, results in a paradox, such that in the case of two passing trains a meter rod is shorter in each train than a meter rod in the other train;

(3) that Einstein's statement that clocks in motion run more slowly than when at rest, considered in the light of his principle of relativity, also results in the paradox: in the case of two passing trains clocks run more slowly on each train than on the other train;

(4) that the theory requires a different redefinition of simultaneity for each velocity that a train may have;

(5) that the alleged slowing of a clock is not caused by motion, as stated by Einstein, but is merely the effect of the redefinition of simulteity;

(6) that according to the theory, under certain circumstances clocks must be regarded as running backward;

(7) that according to the theory events A and B can take place in the order A-B on the ground and in the order B-A on a moving train;

(8) that according to the theory clocks must be endowed with intelligence to know how to respond to the acceleration of a train — depending upon how the origin of the train scale has been arbitrarily assigned;

(9) that according to the theory when the rate of a clock is reduced the flow of time itself is reduced; and that where time is slowed so are bodily processes; and

(10) that the effect of the transformation equations in the case of several beams from a single source is to assign a travel time to each beam exactly in proportion to the distance traveled in a second in a system moving relative to the source, so that the velocity of the beams will come out the same in both systems.

5. CONTRADICTIONS IN THE THEORY

Source on the train. Until now we have been considering the velocities relative to the ground and relative to the train of beams from a source stationary on the ground. Now let us consider beams from a source on the train.

One of the basic postulates of the Einstein theory is that the laws of nature are the same in all inertial systems. According to this postulate, in any inertial system (uniformly moving frame of reference) in which there is a source of light, the beams from that source will behave in the same way that beams behave in any other inertial system when the source of light is in that system. This means that since beams emitted simultaneously from a source on the ground (as one inertial system) reach, in a given interval, points equidistant from the source, it follows from the postulate that in the case of any uniformly moving train (as another inertial system) the same will be true; that is, beams emitted simultaneously from a source on that train will reach, in any given interval, points equidistant from the source as measured along that train.

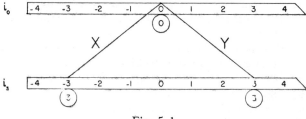

Fig. 5-1

This postulate is illustrated in Fig. 5-1, representing any train in motion but which appears stationary to an observer on the train. The figure shows two beams X and Y emitted at the origin of the train at an instant i_0 and reaching the points -3 and $+3$ on the train (equidistant from the source) at instant i_3, 3 seconds after instant i_0, by the clocks on the train. This is in accord with the Einstein theory and applies to a train moving in any direction at any speed.

Two trains passing. Now let us see the consequences of the application of Einstein's postulate of the uniform laws of nature and of the Einstein transformation equations to the case of two trains passing one another in opposite directions.

Each graph in Fig. 5-2 is a space-time graph representing a westbound train T and an east-bound train R passing one another on parallel tracks. Each train may be considered to be an inertial system. Graph (a) represents the motion of two beams X and Y from a source at rest on train T at its origin. In accord with Einstein's postulate of the uniform laws of nature, beams X and Y, emitted simultaneously from the source on train T, traveling 1 unit per second relative to that train, will reach in 3 seconds the marks -3 and $+3$ on that train, as shown at B and D. It is supposed that $v/c = \frac{1}{3}$.

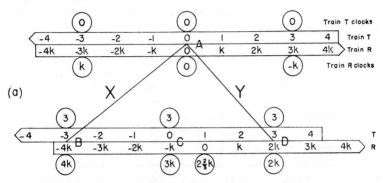

(a)

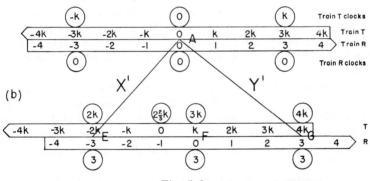

(b)

Fig. 5-2

Now if we apply Einstein's transformation equation (1) in graph (a) we obtain for train R the scale readings of $-4k$ and $2k$ respectively at points B and D, as shown; and if we apply Einstein's transformation equation (2) we obtain for train R clock readings $4k$ and $2k$ at points B and D. Then, using the two-clock method of timing, Einstein would say that according to the train clocks at A and B beam X traveled $4k$ units relative to train R in $4k$ seconds, or 1 unit per second; and that according to the train clocks at A and D beam Y

53

traveled $2k$ units relative to the train in $2k$ seconds, showing that both beams traveled 1 unit per second relative to train R.

On the other hand, if the source of light is on train R, emitting beams X' and Y', as shown in graph (b), we are required by the Einstein theory to assume that when the two trains are in any relative position the clocks on train R will be in synchronism and that in 3 seconds by these clocks beams X' and Y' will reach the marks -3 and $+3$ on train R, as shown by points E and G. Application of the Einstein transformation equations then results in the train T scale values at E and G being respectively $-2k$ and $4k$, and the train T clock readings at these points being respectively $2k$ and $4k$, as shown. Thus, Einstein presumes that, using the two-clock method of timing, the observer on train T will find beam X' to travel $2k$ units in $2k$ seconds and beam Y' to travel $4k$ units in $4k$ seconds; that is, finding each beam to travel 1 unit per second relative to train T.

A contradictory consequence. Now let us say there is a source of light on each train. Then in order to make the velocities of beams X and Y come out equal relative to train R the theory has to assume that when the trains are in any given relative position the train T clocks read the same and the train R clocks all read differently, as shown in graph (a); whereas, in order to make the velocities of beams X' and Y' come out equal relative to train T the theory has to assume that when the trains are in any given relative position the train R clocks all read the same and the train T clocks all read differently, as shown in graph (b).

This means that the theory has to assume that when two trains with a source of light on each passing one another as in Fig. 5-2 are in any given relative position, the clocks on each train all read the same and all read differently.

Here is an impossible consequence of the Einstein theory.

The appearance interpretation fails. Einsteinists have sometimes attempted to explain away this contradiction by invoking the *appearance interpretation* mentioned on page 21, that is, by saying that the train clock readings, $4k$, $3k$, $2k$, etc., shown for the train R clocks in diagram (a) and for the train T clocks in diagram (b), are not presumed by the theory to be actual clock readings (readings obtained in each case by an observer where the clock is) but merely the readings the clocks *appear* to have as seen in each case by an observer *on the other train* — that in accord with their actual readings the clocks on both trains are always in synchronism. This would mean, for example.

that in the case of train R in diagram (a) the actual clock readings, as obtained by an observer on train R, are not $4k$, $3k$, and $2k$, as indicated. This is the *appearance interpretation* which has been discussed previously. But let us review its consequences.

Let the reader choose any clock reading to represent the actual readings of the three clocks on train R in place of the readings $4k$, $3k$, and $2k$. Let us say he chooses $3k$ for all three clocks. By these clock readings the observer on train R would find the velocity of beam X relative to train R to be $4k$ units in $3k$ seconds, and would find the velocity of beam Y relative to train R to be $2k$ units in $3k$ seconds — these being unequal velocities.

Thus we see that unless we assume that according to the theory the observer on train R would obtain in this case unequal clock readings as shown in diagram (a), he would not obtain equal velocities for beams X and Y relative to his train. The contradiction still remains!

Any attempt to explain away the contradiction by means of an appearance interpretation (according to which train clocks merely *appear* to be out of synchronism to an observer *on some other train*) fails because it results in one observer finding that the velocities of the beams are unequal — contrary to the theory.

Supplement 4 (p. 98) explains other contradictions in the theory as seen by the classicist.

Summary. We have now seen that the Einstein theory embodies the following characteristics and assumptions.

1. The assumption that if beams are emitted simultaneously from a source on the ground, the clocks on a moving train are out of synchronism in the sense that when the train is in any given position all the clocks on it read differently.

2. The necessity to use a 'two-clock method of timing' in which the start of the motion of a beam or object is read from one clock and the end of the motion is read from another clock that is not in synchronism with the first.

3. The deduction that when a train is at rest its clocks are in synchronism; whereas, if the train is started forward the clocks got out of synchronism; if the train is then stopped the clocks become synchronized again; and if the train then moves backwards the clocks get out of synchronism in the reverse order.

4. The deduction that when a train is accelerated forward the rear clocks on the train speed up and the forward clocks slow down; whereas, if the train is decelerated the forward clocks speed up and the

55

rear clocks slow down. This differing action must be presumed to take place even though all the clocks on the train are subject to exactly the same movement of the train.

5. The contradiction that if two trains are passing one another with a source of light on each, the clocks on each train must be both in synchronism and out of synchronism.

6. The contradiction that if two trains are moving in opposite directions relative to the earth, each having a source of light, the clocks on the ground must be out of synchronism in both directions at the same time. (Shown in Supplement 4).

7. The deduction that it is possible under certain circumstances that an infinite series of events occuring in succession relative to the ground should be regarded by the theory as occuring at a single instant relative to a moving train.

8. The deduction that it is possible under certain circumstances that an infinite series of events occuring in succession relative to the ground should be regarded by the theory as occuring *in the reverse order* relative to a moving train.

9. Quite apart from all considerations of the requirement of the invalid two-clock method of timing with clocks out of synchronism, of the impossible consequences of the theory, etc., the fact remains that the evidence of the spectroscope and of the aberration of star light disproves the Einstein postulate of the 'constant velocity of light.'

True character of the theory. It is customary to state that according to the Einstein theory the velocity of light *is* constant. This is the case presumably because Einstein himself has repeatedly made this statement. However our analysis of the theory has shown that this statement is not to be taken literally. It misrepresents the true character of the theory, as mentioned earlier.

In his chapter on The Behavior of Measuring-rods and Clocks in Motion, in his *Relativity*, Einstein tells us that according to his theory measuring-rods 'in motion' are shortened and clocks 'in motion' run more slowly. To tell the whole story he should have added "and get out of synchronism," as we have seen. In the light of these pronouncements and in the light of the discussion of Fig. 3-5, for example, it is clear that in essence the Einstein theory does not presume to state that the velocities of beams X and Y in Fig. 3-5 are *actually* equal relative to the train. According to the theory it is merely *that because of the (erratic) "behavior of measuring-rods and clocks in motion" (which is presumed to be unknown to the observer on the train) the measures of distance and time obtained by the observer on the train are rendered*

56

untrue by the motion of the train, so that when the velocities of beams X and Y are inadvertently calculated from these incorrect measures of distance and time, the velocities will come out the same. That is, it is wholly a matter of the mistaken use of incorrect measures. That is all!

An analogy. We could easily make it appear that all men are the same height merely by defining a foot separately for each man as $1/6$ of his height. Using this separate unit in each case, each man's height would come out just 6 ft.

Correspondingly, what the Einstein theory does in effect is merely to define a second separately for each beam of light in each inertial system as the time required for the beam in question to travel 300,000 kilometers relative to that inertial system. Using this definition of a second in each case results, of course, in the velocity of each beam coming out just 300,000 kilometers per second!

6. THE CRITERIA OF VALIDITY

Criteria of validity. It may be well at this point to remind ourselves of the criteria of the validity of a theory. It must be understood at the outset that there are three criteria of the validity of any theory. These are as follows.

1. Is it a rational theory?
2. If so, is it a possible theory?
3. If so, are experimental facts and observations in accord with it?

The first criterion. Here is an example of the application of the first criterion. In the effort to explain the Michelson-Morley experiment without rejecting the ether theory, the thought was advanced that the earth might be stationary in the ether. Coleman applies the rationality criterion to this concept, saying, "Such an idea was not considered seriously, since it would mean in effect that our earth occupied the omnipotent position in the universe, with all the other heavenly bodies paying homage by revolving around it."

Thus we see that an idea is not to be taken seriously if it does not meet the criterion of being rational.

Applying the first criterion to the Einstein theory. In order to apply the criterion of rationality to the Einstein theory let us ask ourselves:

1. Is it rational to conceive that the clocks on a train can be in synchronism with those on the ground when the train is stationary, but that the moment the train starts to move all its clocks get out of synchronism, and if the train backs up its clocks all get out of synchronism in the reverse order?

2. Is it rational to accept the requirement of the theory that the same identical motion of a train can cause clocks at one part of the train to speed up and clocks in another part of the train to slow down?

3. Is it rational to assume that when a scientist measures the velocity of a beam of light he will time the start of the motion of the beam by one clock and time the end of the motion by another clock that is out of synchronsim with the first clock?

4. Is it rational to conceive that two events A and B can occur in the order A - B on the ground but in the order B - A on a moving train?

5. Is it rational to conceive that an infinite series of events occurring in succession relative to the ground can occur at one and only one instant relative to a moving train?

6. Is it rational to conceive that under certain circumstances, as when a train starts to move, certain clocks will run backward?

7. Is it rational to conceive that clocks can know how to respond to the acceleration of a train (differently depending upon where the origin of the train is arbitrarily located)?

Is the theory rational? Can we say yes to answer to all these questions? If not, must we not regard the theory as failing to meet an important criterion of validity? If so, and if we therefore judge the theory unacceptable, is there any need to consider any further criteria?

If, in the light of the above questions, one can still regard the theory as rational, he must still consider the second criterion: Is it a possible theory?

The second criterion. It is well known in logic that if a hypothesis leads unmistakably to a conclusion that is self-contradictory and hence impossible, the hypothesis itself is thereby invalidated. No valid theory can have an impossible consequence. The second criterion is necessary, therefore, because it makes no difference how many experimental facts and observations are in accord with a theory, if the theory is an impossible one because it leads to impossible consequences, the theory is still unacceptable.

For example, let us say a theory has been advanced to account for one of the stars of a binary system being brighter than its sister star — the theory being that the brighter star is hotter and that it is hotter because it is revolving around its sister star more often than the sister star revolves around it. What would we think of such a theory? We would probably say it deserves no consideration whatsoever because it is an impossible theory. (It would be an impossible theory, of course, because one binary star could not revolve around its sister star more often than the sister star revolves around it.) Being an impossible theory it would be unacceptable. Hence the need for the second criterion.

Impossible consequence. By an impossible consequence is meant, for example, one in which some condition must both be and not be — such as the consequence that the motion of a source must be imparted to its beams and yet not be imparted to its beams; or that two beams must both separate and remain together; or that a row of clocks must all read the same and yet all read differently.

Applying the second criterion. In applying the second criterion (Is it a possible theory?) to the Einstein theory, let us recall that we found that because each of two inertial systems is equally in motion relative to the other it follows from the theory that

(1) the units of distance measure in each system are shorter than those in the other — which is impossible;

(2) the clocks of each system must be regarded as running more slowly than those of the other — which is impossible;

(3) in each of two trains passing one another (Fig. 5-2) the clocks must be both in synchronism and out of synchronism.

These differences according to the theory must be *actual* and hence all attempts to explain away the contradictions by the 'apperance interpretation' fail.

An unacceptable theory. We have seen that the second criterion of the validity of a theory is whether it is a possible theory, and that any theory that has contradictory consequences is an impossible theory and cannot be regarded as valid no matter how much scientific evidence seems to support it. In the light of this criterion and in the light of the contradictions just seen in the Einstein theory, the classicist considers the theory to be unacceptable and hence to be set aside.

Accord with experiment and observation. It is often said that the Einstein theory is in accord with more experimental results and facts of observation than any other theory, and that it is therefore to be considered the most acceptable theory. It is true that the Einstein theory is in accord with more results of experiment and observation than any other theory of light transmission. The error in the deduction that it is therefore the best theory is made clear by the following analogy.

Analogy. Let us say evidence A supports the theory that the core of the earth is solid; evidence B supports the theory that the core is molten; and evidence C supports the theory that it is gaseous.

Let us say some one comes up with the theory that the core of the earth is solid, molten, and gaseous! That theory would be in accord with evidence A, evidence B and evidence C. Does that make it the most acceptable? Obviously not because it claims too much — the core of the earth cannot be solid and yet molten, and yet gaseous!

Now the Einstein theory affirms that the velocities of beams from a given source are constant (a) relative to their source, (b) relative to the cosmos, and (c) relative to any observer. It is therefore in accord with any interferometer experiment which supports the concept that the velocity of light is constant relative to its source; it is in accord with the seeming evidence of binary stars that the velocity of light is constant relative to an ether; and it is in accord with any evidence that might be advanced in support of the concept that the velocity of light is constant relative to any observer.

But it is in a class with theory that the core of the earth is solid, molten, and gaseous. It claims too much.

Let us not say, therefore, that the Einstein theory is our best theory of light transmission because it is in accord with the most scientific evidence — when the evidence is contradictory.

The third criterion. In regard to the third criterion of the validity of a theory we must remember the following.

1. When an experimental result is found to be in agreement with a given theory, we may say that the result *supports* the theory; but we may *not* say that the result *confirms* the theory — meaning to prove the theory true — when there is any possibility that the theory may be disproven by some other evidence; and theoretically this is almost always possible.

2. The greater the number of experimental results that support a theory, the greater is the probability that the theory represents reality — provided it is rational and has no impossible consequences.

3. The deduction from an experimental result is no more valid than the least valid assumption underlying the deduction. For example, in interpreting the null result of an interferometer experiment we may be faced with the choice of assuming that the velocity of reflection from a mirror equals the velocity of incidence either (1) relative to the ether, or (2) relative to the mirror — these being contradictory assumptions. In such a case the deduction is no more valid than the chosen assumption. If the assumption chosen is untrue, the deduction from the experiment is an inconclusive one.*

4. Finally let us remember that it makes no difference how many experimental results or observations are in accord with a given theory, if the theory leads to contradictory consequences, it is invalid to begin with and may as well be disregarded.

Applying the third criterion. In applying the third criterion to the Einstein theory let us remember that

(1) the Einstein 'principle of relativity' (according to which uniform motion in a straight line is relative only and the laws of nature

*It is shown later (p. 74) that the Michelson-Morley experiment is inconclusive because the correct interpretation of the result depends upon the correctness of one or the other of the two contrary assumptions.

are the same in all inertial systems) is supported by many experimental observations, but

  (2) the postulate of 'the constant velocity of light' has been proven false

  (a) by the aberration of starlight,
  (b) by the evidence of the spectroscope when in motion relative to a fixed star — by virtue of the orbital motion of the earth, and indeed,
  (c) by the very definition of relative motion.

The theory invalid. We saw that the third criterion did not need to be applied to the Einstein theory because the theory failed in the first two criteria. However, it even fails the third criterion because one of its basic postulate is disproven in three ways. Is it not time, therefore, to set the theory aside?

Oddly enough, more than one Einsteinist has said to the author, in effect: "It is true that the Einstein theory is contrary to common sense; but we have to accept it because it has been so completely confirmed."

The next section discusses some alleged confirmations of the theory and each is shown not to confirm the theory or even one of its deductions.

Summary of Section 6. In this section it has been shown:

  (1) that there are three criteria of the acceptability of a theory, these being:

  Is it a rational theory?
  If so, is it a possible theory?
  If so, are experimental facts and observations in accord with it?

  (2) that in several respects the theory has unrealistic consequences (such as that a series of events happening in succession on the ground could happen simultaneously on a train) which render it unacceptable.

  (3) that in several respects the theory has contradictory consequences, which therefore render it unacceptable;

  (4) that in view of the theory proving to be irrational and impossible, it makes no difference how many experimental facts and observations appear to support the theory. (Indeed, it was shown in Section 2 that the evidence of the aberration of starlight and the evidence of the spectroscope actually disprove the basic postulate of the theory.)

7. SOME ALLEGED CONFIRMATIONS

Among the alleged confirmations of the Einstein special theory of relativity are (1) the increase in mass of charged particles accelerated in an electric field in accord with Einstein's prediction, (2) the Fizeau experiment, and (3) the life of mesons.

Relation of mass to velocity. From the basic transformation equations (1) and (2) Einstein has derived an equation according to which if a particle is in motion in an inertial system its 'mass' is greater than the mass it would have if at rest in that system. The mass m of the particle when in motion with velocity v is presumed by the theory to be related to its 'rest mass' m_0 in accord with the equation:

Mass (in motion) $= k$ x Rest mass

or
$$m = km_0 \tag{3}$$

in which $k = 1/\sqrt{(1 - v^2/c^2)}$.

Since a body can have one velocity relative to the ground and another velocity relative to a moving train, it follows according to the theory that a body can have one 'mass' relative to the ground and another 'mass' relative to the train.

We see that the nearer the velocity v of a particle approaches the velocity c of light, the greater is the value of k. Indeed, if $v = c$ the value of k becomes infinity — according to which if a particle moved with the velocity of light relative to a given inertial system it would have infinite 'mass' relative to that system.

Since the classicist cannot accept the Einstein theory, he has reason to doubt the validity of any equation such as equation (3) that is derived from it.

The classisist's view. If we think of *mass* as meaning quantity of matter or inertia (its traditional definition), it is easy to show in accord with the concept of the universality of time that the motion of a particle relative to an inertial system cannot have any effect upon its mass as measured in that system. Let us see why this is so.

Graph (a) in Fig. 7-1 represents the inelastic collision of two identical particles P and Q in a system S. We see the particles at 1 and 3 at instant 0; they collide at 2 at instant 1 and remain there, because their momenta are equal and opposite.

Graph (b) shows the same collision of the same particles in the same system S, colliding at 2 and remaining there; but shows a passing system S', which, of course, has no effect upon the collision.

Nevertheless, any phenomenon that occurs in system S also occurs in system S'. Graph (c) shows how the collision occurs in system S'. That is, we see by both graphs (b) and (c) that at instant 0 the particles are at 6 and 8 of system S'; at instant 1 they collide at 6, but are at 5 at instant 2.

Graph (c) makes it clear that in system S' during the first second (instant 0 to instant 1) particle P remains stationary at 6; whereas, particle Q moves 2 units from 8 to 6. Hence if the motion of a particle relative to an inertial system caused it to have an increased mass, it would follow that in system S' particle Q has more mass than particle P.

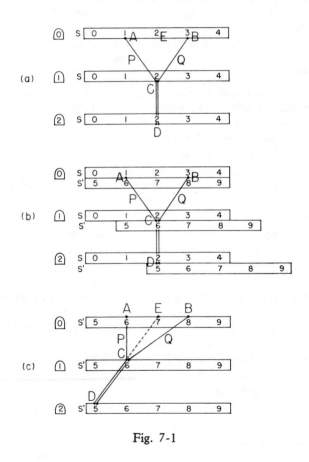

Fig. 7-1

Velocity of the center of mass. We know that in the case of any collision the velocity of the center of mass of the colliding bodies is the same before the collision as after. Extending the line CD to E, we know that the line EC represents the same velocity of the coalesced particles as the line CD and so represents the motion of the center of mass of the particles before the collision. This means that at instant 0 the center of mass was at E in system S', the same as in system S. And since the point E is equidistant from the points A and B at which the particles were at instant 0, it follows that the masses of the particles are equal in system S' as well as in system S.

There can be any number of inertial systems, S', S'', S''', etc., moving to the right or left relative to the system S in which the velocities of the particles are equal. In all these other systems the velocities of the particles will be unequal. Yet the motions of these system will have no effect upon the phenomenon. Hence, as shown in the figure, if the center of mass is midway between the particles in system S it will be also in all the other systems — showing that the two particles have equal masses in all the systems and that therefore the motion of a particle relative to an inertial system cannot change its mass.

Nothing to do with velocity. It is shown in the first edition of this booklet that it is only the redefining of simultaneity in system S' which makes it appear that in system S' particles P and Q have unequal masses, and hence that this effect has nothing to do with the relative velocities of the two particles in system S', even according to the Einstein theory.

Motion does not increase mass. The above reasoning is sufficient to indicate to the classicist that the mere motion of a particle in an inertial system does not cause it to have any more mass than it has when at rest in that system; and that Einstein's equation $m = km_0$, indicating that the mass of a particle in motion in a system is k times the mass it has when at rest in that system is merely a mathematical derivation from the transformation equations of the theory which have been shown to lead to contradictory consequences and therefore cannot be regarded as representing reality.

The inertia of internal kinetic energy. We know that a gyroscope with its rotor at high speed has a high inertia of a sort — a high resistance to a certain deflection of its orientation. Let us imagine, then, that the large amount of energy that in a cyclotron is imparted to a charged particle, over and above that required to give it acceleration (in

65

accord with the equation $KE = \frac{1}{2}mv^2$) gives the particle an internal kinetic energy which manifests itself as inertia — having an effect corresponding to an increase in mass (quantity of matter). This concept, then, would account for the increase in inertia of the particle that accompanies its acceleration in the cyclotron.

Collision of charged particles. Let us now apply what we learned from Fig 7-1 to the case of the collision of charged particles.

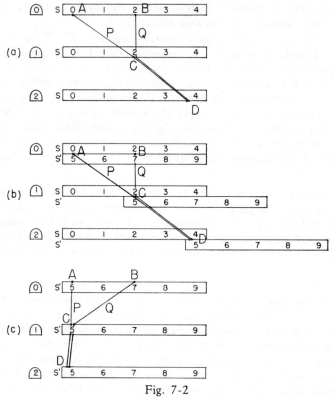

Fig. 7-2

Graph (a) in Fig. 7-2 represents the inelastic collision of two particles, P and Q, in a system S representing a laboratory, relative to which particle Q is at rest and particle P is at high speed, having been accelerated in an electric field by the energy of an oscillator. (For convenience we assume that it is possible for particles P and Q to collide inelastically.) It is assumed that by virtue of the large amount of internal energy that particle P receives while it is being accelerated its inertia is great enough so that it can pick up particle Q and carry it along almost with-

66

out diminution of its velocity. (The velocity of the coalesced particles after collision, represented by space-time line CD, is almost as great as the velocity of particle P before the collision represented by AC, enabling the coalesced particles to nearly reach 4 of the scale.)

Transforming the collision. Now let us assume that during this action a system S' (the system in which particle P is at rest) moves to the right relative to system S, as shown in graph (b). The motion of this system relative to the laboratory has no effect, of course, upon the phenomenon in the laboratory. (Particle P picks upon particle Q at 2 in system S and carries it to nearly 4.)

Now let us see what happens in system S'.

As shown in both graphs (b) and (c), particle P is at rest at 5 of system S' and particle Q starts from 7 and collides with particle P at 5; but after the collision the coalesced particles move only from 5 to a little to the left of 5 in system S'.

Now according to Einstein's mass-velocity equation, $m = km_0$ (equation 3 above), particle Q, by virtue of its high speed in system S' should have had far more inertia than particle P, which is at rest in that system, and should have been able, therefore, to pick up particle P and carry it nearly to 3 of the scale (that is, with almost the same velocity that it had before the collision).

But we see that what actually happens in system S' is that even though particle P is at rest in system S' it is able, by virtue of the inertia of the energy imparted to it during its acceleration, to stop particle Q almost 'dead in its track'.

This demonstration is sufficient to convince the classicist that the motion of particle P relative to the laboratory—just as motion alone— did not cause particle P to have increased inertia in system S — or as is said, more 'mass' than particle Q. He is convinced that it is the 'internal energy' imparted to particle P during its acceleration that gives it the increased inertia; and that this is true in both system S and system S'.

Causal and functional relationships. The classicist regards as more or less incidental the fact that during the buildup of internal energy in particle P there was also an increase in the velocity of particle P relative to system S (the laboratory). (The increase in the inertia of the particle took place without any acceleration of the particle in the system in which it remained at rest.)

We may say, then, that in the particular case of a charged particle being accelerated in a cyclotron there is incidentally a *functional* relation between increase in velocity and increase in inertia (in the laboratory only — not in the system in which the particle is at rest). But there

67

is no causal relation — the acceleration as such did not *create* the increase in inertia.

An analogy. The distinction between a causal relation and a mere functional relation may be clarified, perhaps, by means of an analogy. If an athlete runs around a track we might say that there is a functional relation between the distance he runs and the amount he perspires; but this is not a causal relation (the distance does not cause the perspiration) because if the athlete made the same running motions in a treadmill he would presumable perspire just as much — showing that it was the physical exercise and not the distance covered over the ground that caused the perspiring. We must be careful not to draw hasty conclusions as to causal relations when we have only functional relations as the basis for judgment.

Mistaken reasoning? In view of the above findings it appears to the classicist that those who consider the behavior of charged particles in acceleration to confirm the Einstein mass-velocity equation may fail to properly distinguish between a causal relation and a mere functional relation. They may assume, merely because there is an incidental functional relation between velocity and inertia in the special case of charged particles in a cyclotron, mass spectrograph, or the like, that the velocity is the cause of the increase in inertia. This mistaken reasoning might be occasioned in part because Einstein had deduced an equation in his theory which he interpreted as indicating a causal relation — that an increase in the velocity of *any* particle relative to any inertial system can cause an increase in its inertia.

Conclusion. In the light of the above reasoning the classicist may conclude that the behavior of charged particles does not confirm the Einstein mass-velocity equation, and consequently does not confirm his theory.

Acceleration of a rocket. If we can rid ourselves of a notion that mere relative motion — apart from the impartation of energy, as from an oscillator to a charged particle — can cause an increment in the mass of a moving body, we are then in position to abandon the Einstein concept that no object can have a velocity greater than *c* relative to any inertial system.

This would mean that we may conceive that if a rocket could be accelerated indefinately it could attain a velocity relative to the earth greater than *c*. For example, let us suppose that with nuclear power a rocket could be given an acceleration of 1 kilometer per second each second. In one day it would acquire a velocity of 86,400 km. per, sec., in two days a velocity of 172,800 km. per sec., etc. At this rate it would acquire the speed of light relative to the earth in about 35 days. Since no energy is being 'pumped' into the rocket by an oscillator or other source, we can assume that it would have no increase in mass and that the same acceleration could continue indefinitely regardless of velocity. In that case in 350 days the rocket could attain a velocity of 10 times the velocity of light. Jet planes attain a speed of several times that of sound even in spite of a 'sound barrier'; but there would be no barrier in the case of the accelerated rocket, assuming space to be 'empty'.

It would seem desirable, therefore, in this age of space travel that we get clear-minded regarding any alleged limitation to the speed of space travel.

Alleged confirmation by the Fizeau experiment. In his *Relativity* Einstein presents specifically only one experimental finding in support of his special theory of relativity. His reasoning warrents careful examination.

One of the deductions of Einstein's theory is his 'theorem of the addition of velocities', according to which if an inertial system S' has a velocity v relative to an inertial system S and a particle P has a velocity w in the same direction in system S', the velocity W of P relative to system S is not $v + w$, as classical physics would have it; but according to the theory.

$$W = \frac{v + w}{1 + vw/c^2}$$

Einstein states (p. 45) that his theorem of the addition of velocities is "most elegantly confirmed" by the Fizeau experiment on the velocity of light in a flowing liquid.

In the Fizeau experiment a liquid was caused to flow with velocity v relative to the laboratory and light from a source stationary in the laboratory was caused to shine through the liquid in the direction of its flow. The experiment was to determine the velocity of the light relative to the laboratory in its passage through the liquid, the velocity w of light relative to the liquid when stationary being known as a function of the index of refraction.

Now Einstein says (p. 47), "In accordance with the principle of relativity we shall certainly have to take for granted that the propagation of light always takes place with the same velocity w *with respect to the liquid*, whether the latter is in motion with reference to other bodies or not." (Ital. his.)

There is error of reasoning in the statement just quoted. Here is why. Einstein uses the expression 'principle of relativity' to refer to his postulate that the laws of nature are the same in all inertial systems. According to that postulate it follows that if the velocity of light relative to the liquid (as the light flows through the liquid) is w when the liquid and source of light are at rest in the laboratory (inertial system S) it will be true also that the velocity of light relative to the liquid will be w in the inertial system S' in which the liquid is at rest (when flowing relative to the laboratory) if the source of light *is also at rest in that system* (S'). That is, it follows from the principle of relativity that in any inertial system in which the source of light and the liquid are both stationary, the velocity of the light in the liquid from that source will be w. But it does *not* follow from the principle of relativity that if the source is in one system (S, the laboratory) and the liquid is in another inertial system (S', that of the liquid when flowing relative to the laboratory) the velocity of the light relative to the liquid will be w. (We have but to realize that if the liquid could move away from the source at the velocity c, the light could not have any velocity relative to the liquid.)

Fizeau found that when the liquid flowed relative to the laboratory but the source of light remained at rest in the laboratory the velocity of the light relative to the liquid was reduced by an amount expressed by vw^2/c^2. Einstein showed that this was approximately ("to within one percent") the amount of reduction that would be expected in accord with his equation $W = (v + w)/(1 + vw/c^2)$. He assumed, therefore, that the Fizeau result 'confirmed' his equation for the addition of velocities.

To the classicist it seems much more reasonable to assume that with the liquid and source in two different inertial systems the velocity of the light would not be w relative to the liquid to start with (as Einstein took for granted) since in that case the light would enter the liquid with the velocity $c - v$ relative to the liquid. In that case the application of Einstein's equation for the addition of velocities would yield a result that did not agree with the Fizeau result — thereby completely invalidating Einstein's reasoning by which he contended that the Fizeau result confirmed his equation.

The life of mesons. Mesons (cosmic rays) originating in the upper atmosphere have different velocities as they decend to the earth and correspondingly different periods of decay. (Reference is generally made to what are known as *mu* mesons which are derived from *pi* mesons and which have varying velocities because of the varying division of the energy of the *pi* meson between the *mu* meson and the nutrino resulting from the *pi* meson).

Of any two mesons having different velocities v, their life spans are believed to vary in proportion to $1\sqrt{(1 - v^2/c^2)}$ — the greater the velocity, the longer the life. And this observation is often cited as confirming the Einstein deduction that the rates of clocks in motion vary in proportion to $\sqrt{(1 - v^2/c^2)}$, the idea being that if each meson timed its life span by a clock of its own the longer life spans (because of greater velocity) would be timed by clocks running correspondingly more slowly (because of the greater velocity) and the result would be that all the mesons would time their life span the same amount!

The classicist's comment is: Quite an interesting coincidence — just as it was a coincidence that Lorentz's theory of the contraction of atoms in their line of motion should seemingly compensate for the expected difference in the velocity of light in the two arms of the Michelson-Morley interferometer or the coincidence that the increase in inertia of a charged particle in a cyclotron due to the impartation of energy to the particle should happen to be just that expected in the Einstein theory as the result of mere relative motion.

The fact remains, of course, that the mesons do have varying energies and do have varying velocities and it would seem that the varying energies are sufficient to account for the varying velocities and that the varying velocities are sufficient to account for the varying life spans. In the light of these facts the classicist sees no need to pretend that there is any reason to think of the life spans of mesons as being equal. He considers it mere pretense, therefore, that the coincidence mentioned above constitutes any confirmation of the Einstein concept of the slowing of moving clocks.

This is true particularly since the Einstein concept of the slowing of moving clocks leads to an impossible consequence which renders it unacceptable anyway.

Summary of Section 7 .In this section it has been shown:

(1) that the emperical evidence most often cited by Einsteinists in support of the Einstein theory are the 'increase in mass with velocity' in the case of charged particles and the life of mesons;

(2) that in both cases an alternative explanation, satisfactory to the classicist, can be given, quite apart from the Einstein theory; and

(3) that the only evidence in support of his theory described by Einstein in his *Relativity* is the result of the Fizeau experiment with light in a flowing liquid; and that Einstein's reasoning in this case was found to be at fault, thereby invalidating his contention that the Fizeau

71

result confirmed his theory. (Einstein mentions the aberration of starlight as supporting his theory but does not explain how).

The advance of the perihelion of Mercury and the bending of light rays in a gravitational field. It is customary in encyclopedias and elsewhere to cite the advance of the perihelion of Mercury and the bending of light rays in a gravitational field as emperical evidence confirming the Einstein special theory of relativity. This is a mistake because Einstein discusses the "Motion of the perihelion of Mercury" and the "Deflection of light by a gravitational field" in his *Relativity* only in his Appendix III, which is entitled "The experimental confirmation of the general theory of relativity." The manner in which the bending of light rays in a gravitational field is presumed by Einstein to confirm his general theory of relativity is explained in detail in the Appendix.

8. PERTINENT EXPERIMENTS

Experiments bearing on the ether and source theories. It is not within the scope of this booklet to discuss at length the various experiments that have a bearing upon the choice between the ether theory and source theory. But three important experiments merit special comment. These are the Michelson-Morley experiment, the Kennedy-Thorndike experiment, and the Majorana experiment with a moving source.

Defining the ether theory. In order to evaluate these experiments it is necessary to have a clear understanding of the ether theory and the assumptions attending it.

Let us define the ether theory as the theory according to which the velocity of light, *upon issuance from any source,* whether moving or stationary, is constant relative to a medium called the ether, regarded as stationary in the cosmos.

This definition of the ether theory clearly avoids any assumption as to what may happen to the velocity of light upon being reflected from a mirror. This is necessary because there are two possible assumptions regarding the velocity of reflected light which are contradictory although each is quite in harmony with the ether theory as defined.

The first assumption. One such assumption is that the velocity of light reflected from a mirror is equal to the velocity of the incident light *relative to the mirror* — in accord with the concept of the conservation of energy within an inertial system and in accord with the principle of relativity. In accord with this assumption if the mirror is in motion relative to the ether the velocity of the reflected light is greater or less than that of the incident light *relative to the ether.*

The second assumption. The other assumption is that the velocity of reflection from a mirror is equal to the velocity of incidence *relative to the ether.* In accord with this assumption the velocity of reflected light would always be c relative to the ether whether the mirror moved in the ether or not. And in accord with this assumption the velocity of reflection would be greater or less than the velocity of incidence *relative to the mirror.*

Designating two ether theories. For convenience let us designate as *ether theory 1* the ether theory as defined together with the first assumption regarding the velocity of reflection, and designate as *ether theory 2* the ether theory as defined together with the second assumption regarding reflection velocity. Let it be understood that both *ether theory 1* and *ether theory 2* assume that the classical concept of the addition of velocities applies to all velocities including velocities of light.

Michelson-Morley experiment inconclusive. It would appear that the null result of the Michelson-Morley experiment is universally regarded as proving that the velocity of light from a source at rest on the earth is constant (the same in all directions) relative to the earth, and that this result therefore contradicts any ether theory. But this is a mistaken deduction for the following reasons. Fig. 8-1 represents an interferometer with a source of light S emitting a beam in the direction SA, the beam being divided by the half silvered mirror A of the interferometer into two halves, one reflected along the path ABA and the other following the path ACA — the two half beams uniting at A and proceeding to the telescope at D.

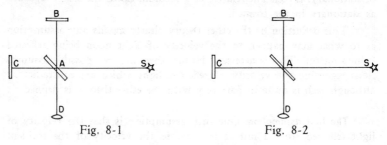

Fig. 8-1   Fig. 8-2

It is customary to evaluate the null results of the theory by a consideration of *ether theory 2* only — disregarding *ether theory 1*. Let us say the laboratory (which carries both interferometer and source of light) is moving through the ether in the direction AS with the velocity v. Then in accord with *ether theory 2* and in accord with the classical concept of the addition of velocities, the velocity of the light relative to the interferometer is $c + v$ in the path AC and $c - v$ in the path CA: whereas in both paths AB and BA the velocity of the light relative to the interferometer is $\sqrt{(c^2 - v^2)}$. It can be shown that in this case it takes longer for the light to travel the path ACA than to travel the path ABA, whereas if the interferometer is rotated 90° in either direction the reverse is true, and that this rotation will cause a fringe shift. Since the expected fringe shift was not observed ('null result') *ether theory 2* is disproven.

But now let us consider *ether theory 1*. Again let us suppose first that the laboratory is moving in the direction AS relative to the ether with velocity v. Then according to *ether theory 1* and in accord with

74

the classical concept of the addition of velocities, the velocity of the beam along the path SA is $c + v$ relative to the interferometer; and the velocity of each half beam along paths ABA and ACA is also $c + v$. That is, the light has the same velocity relative to the interferometer along both paths.

If the apparatus is then rotated 90° in either direction, the velocity of the light along the path SA is approximately c (theoretically $\sqrt{(c^2 - v^2)}$), and according to *ether theory 1* this will be the velocity of both half beams along the paths ABA and ACA.

A fringe shift will be observed upon rotation of the apparatus only in case there is a change in the ratio of the velocities of the two half beams in paths ABA and ACA. But we have just seen that in accord with *ether theory 1* there would be no such change of ratio; hence in accord with *ether theory 1* we would expect the null result that was obtained.

This means that the null result of the Michelson-Morley experiment — although contrary to *ether theory 2* — is in accord with both the source theory and *ether theory 1*. Hence this experiment is inconclusive as between the source theory and *ether theory 1*.

Although the Michelson-Morley null result is seen not to rule out what we called *ether theory 1*, it can be said, nevertheless, to *support* the source theory. This is so because if the source theory is true we would expect a null result from the Michelson-Morley experiment. Moreover it may be said that to the extent that we may consider the central mirror of the Michelson-Morley interferometer as the source of the light traveling the paths AB and AC, then the null result shows that beams from a source at rest relative to the ground have equal velocities relative to the ground in the two directions at right angles.

Since assumption 2 regarding the velocity of reflection is contradicted by the experiment, we may consider that this experiment supports assumption 1, according to which the velocity of reflection from a mirror is equal to the velocity of incidence *relative to the mirror* — regardless of whether the velocity of light issuing from its source is constant relative to its source or relative to an ether. Fortunately, this is a very important deduction from the Michelson-Morley experiment, which will be of help in the interpretation of other interferometer experiments.

The Kennedy-Thorndike experiment[1] made use of an interferometer having unequal arms, as represented in Fig. 8-2. Rotation of such an apparatus will yield a fringe shift in accord with *ether theory 1* for

[1] *Phys. Rev.* Vol. 42, p. 400 (1932)

the following reason. Let the laboratory (and source) first move through the ether in the direction AS, causing the light along the path SA to have the velocity $c + v$ relative to the interferometer with a wavelength w_1 such that $w_1 = (c + v)\, w/c$, w being the wavelength of similar light from a source at rest in the ether. In accord with *ether theory 1* the velocity of the light in both paths ABA and ACA will be $c + v$ relative to the interferometer. Hence in both these paths the wavelength of the beams will be w_1 as in path SA.

Let d represent the difference in the lengths of the paths ABA and ACA. In accord with *ether theory 1* the number n_1, of waves in the distance $d = d/w_1$.

Now as the apparatus is rotated through 90° the velocity of the light in the path SA relative to the interferometer (*by ether theory 1*) is reduced from $c + v$ to approximately c, and the wavelength is reduced in proportion to a new and lesser value w_2. This enables the distance d (in the longer path) to hold a greater number n_2 of waves.

Now any change in the number of waves in distance d causes a fringe shift. The number of fringes shifting $= n_2 - n_1$.

This means that in accord with *ether theory 1* we would expect the Kennedy-Thorndike experiment to result in a fringe shift. However, these scientists report a virtual "null result", which therefore contradicts *ether theory 1*.

We have just seen that *ether theory 2*, involving the concept that the velocity of reflection equals the velocity of incidence relative to the ether, has been found incompatible with the null result of the Michelson-Morley experiment. If we discard that theory we may say that the Kennedy-Thorndike experiment contradicts the ether theory as a whole.

The null result supports the source theory because according to that theory rotation of the apparatus would cause no change in the wavelength of the light and hence no fringe shift.

The Majorana experiment. In the Majorana experiment[2] with a moving source of light, the arms of the interferometer were of unequal length as in the Kennedy-Thorndike experiment (Fig. 8-2), differing by the distance d, let us say. In this experiment the apparatus was not rotated but the source S of light was moved first toward and then away from the interferometer, so that according to the *ether theory 1* there would first be a shortening of the wavelength of the light and then a lengthening of the wavelength — as opposed to no change in wavelength in accord with the source theory — thus causing a change in the

---

[2] Q. Majorana, *Phil. Mag.*, Vol. 37, p. 145 (1919)

number of waves in the distance d and hence causing a fringe shift when the motion of the source was reversed.

Majorana reports having observed just the amount of fringe shift that would be expected in accord with *ether theory 1* as the result of the reversal of the motion of the source. His finding therefore supports the *ether theory 1* and contradicts the source theory.

Thus we find the Michelson-Morley experiment in support of both the ether theory and source theory; we find the Kennedy-Thorndike experiment in support of the source theory but contradicting the ether theory; and we find the Majorana experiment supporting the the ether theory and contradicting the source theory.

Other evidence of experiment and observation results in similarity contradictory support of the source and ether theories.

Further research needed. In the opinion of the author these contradictory findings point definitely to the need for further research on the velocity of light.

Here follow three suggested experiments which might help in the solution of the problem of light velocity.

A suggested experiment. Here is one suggested experiment which differs slightly from the Majorana experiment described. Let the wavelength of light be investigated by means of an interferometer with arms of unequal length, as in the Majorana experiment. But instead of using a moving terrestrial source let the comparison be made between the light from the approaching limb of the sun and the light from the receding limb, the light passing through a prism to obtain monochromatic light.

We know that in the case of monochromatic light there would be no difference according to the source theory in the wavelength of light whether coming from the approaching limb or the receding limb of the sun; whereas, according to the ether theory a shift of source from one limb to the other would cause a difference in wavelength. The difference in wavelength so caused would be expected to cause a shift of interference fringes in the interferometer. Hence, if we accept the null result of the Michelson-Morley experiment as indicating that the velocity of reflection from a mirror equals the velocity of incidence relative to the mirror, as explained above, then a null result of this suggested experiment (no fringe shift) would uphold the source theory, whereas a fringe shift of the amount expected in accord with the ether theory would uphold that theory.

A second suggested experiment. A number of investigators have measured the velocity of light by the Kerr cell method, comparable to the toothed-wheel method of Fizeau. This is one in which a ray of light is projected from a source to a mirror and back to a telescope. The ray is interrupted periodically by one Kerr cell as it leaves the source (in the laboratory) and by another Kerr cell as it enters the telescope, the interruptions being rendered simultaneous by fluctuations of voltage of the same oscillator. Whereas Fizeau's toothed wheel could interrupt the ray a few thousand times a second, the Kerr cell can interrupt it many millions of times a second. If the light travels the distance to the mirror and back in just half the interval between interruptions, the light passing through the first Kerr cell will be stopped by the second and not seen in the telescope. The velocity of the light relative to the laboratory is therefore the light path multiplied by 2 times the frequency of the oscillator.

For our present purpose it is not necessary to obtain a measure of the velocity of the light, but merely to detect any change in that velocity that might be caused by a change in the orientation of the apparatus. Thus according to the source theory the velocity of the ray will be c relative to the source and relative to the laboratory on its way to the mirror and c relative to the mirror and the laboratory on its way back regardless of the orientation; whereas according to the ether theory, if the laboratory is moving eastward with velocity v relative to the ether and the light shines eastward from the source the velocity of the light relative to the laboratory will be $c - v$ relative to the laboratory — in both directions according to the concept of the equal velocity of incidence and reflection relative to a mirror — whereas, if the light shines westward from the source, the velocity of the light relative to the laboratory will be $c + v$.

The method is to adjust the frequency of the oscillator so that the light is visible in the telescope, then change the orientation of the apparatus. If there is any slight change in the velocity of the light relative to the laboratory the light will be immediately rendered invisible A change of velocity will support the ether theory. No change will support the source theory.

Indeed, it may be safely assumed that the rotation of the earth produces an appreciable reorientation of the apparatus relative to the ether. Hence in accord with the ether theory we would expect a continuous change of velocity of the light relative to the laboratory. In that case it would be impossible with any constant frequency of the oscillator to make the light remain visible in the telescope.

Support for the source theory. No such variation has been reported by the investigators using the Kerr cell method; hence we may regard their experiments as supporting the source theory — that the motion of a source is imparted to its beams and that the successive wave fronts from a source remain concentric.

A third suggested experiment. It would seem possible to use the Kerr cell apparatus in another experiment if it is possible by means of a telescope to direct the light of the sun into the Kerr cell apparatus. The method would be to point the telescope first at the approaching limb of the sun and then gradually move it to point to the receding limb. According to the ether theory there should be no difference in the velocity of light from the two limbs; whereas, according to the source theory there should be a difference. If the Kerr cell apparatus could detect this difference in velocity this would not only support the source theory but it would disprove the Einstein postulate of the constant velocity of light. A null result would contradict the source theory but it would not distinguish between the ether theory and the Einstein theory — it would support both.)

An alternative method would be to keep the telescope pointed directly at the center of the sun's disc and note whether the apparatus showed any difference in the velocity of the sunlight between morning (when the telescope approached the sun) and afternoon (when the telescope receded from the sun). In this case, if it were certain that the apparatus should be sensitive enough to retect the difference in velocity expected by classical theory, a null result would contradict the classical law of the addition of velocities; whereas, an observed difference in velocity, although not distinguishing between the ether theory and the source theory unless the velocities were actually measured, would nevertheless contradict the postulate of the 'constant velocity of light'

Other experiments. There are undoubtedly other experiments — possibly better ones — that can be devised to help us decide between the ether theory and the source theory.

Summary. It has been shown in this booklet:

(1) that the two theories of light velocity — the ether theory and the source theory — are incompatible; only one can represent reality regarding the velocity of light. Either the velocity of a source of light is imparted to its beams (source theory) or it is not (ether theory);

(2) that scientific evidence is inconclusive — some supports the ether theory and some supports the source theory;

(3) that the Einstein theory, which purports to harmonize the evidence by explaining how the velocity of light can be constant relative to the cosmos and at the same time relative to its source, though the source is moving in the cosmos, has contradictory consequences, making it an impossible theory and hence unacceptable;

(4) that quite apart from the consideration of contradictory consequences, the theory requires us to consider that under certain circumstances an infinite series of events occurring in succession in one inertial system must be regarded by the theory as occurring at a single instant in another inertial system — a concept which the classicist considers to be unthinkable and in no way representing reality.

(5) that the aberration of starlight and evidence of the spectroscope definitely show the velocity of light relative to the earth to be variable — thus disproving Einstein's postulate of the 'constant velocity of light.'

(6) that Einstein's postulate of the 'constant velocity of light' was based upon the mistaken concept that the classical law of the addition of velocities is in conflict with the 'principle of relativity' — showing that this postulate was not needed in the first place;

(7) that the behavior of charged particles in a cyclotron and mass spectrograph, which is often stated as confirming the Einstein theory, can be explained without recourse to the Einstein theory. This behavior, therefore, does not confirm the theory;

(8) that the problem of the velocity of light — whether constant relative to an ether or relative to its source — is still unsolved and remains a challenge to young physicists.

Suggestions were made as to possible experiments that would throw light upon the choice between the ether theory and source theory.

A tentative theory of relativity is now offered which is in accord with Einstein's postulates of the relativity of motion and the uniformity of the laws of nature in all inertial systems. It is also in accord with the classical concept of the universality of time. Perforce, it embraces the source theory and rejects the concept of an ether.

9. A CLASSICAL THEORY OF RELATIVITY

A classical theory of relativity. In view of the fact that Einstein's postulates of the relativity of motion and of the uniformity of the laws of nature are so universally accepted, but in view also of the finding of this booklet that Einstein's postulate of the "constant velocity of light" has proven to be untenable, a classical theory of relativity* is herein proposed whose three basic postulates are the following.

1. All straight-line motion at uniform rate is relative only — Einstein. There is no ether to constitute an inertial system at absolute rest and with respect to which motion might be regarded as absolute.

2. The laws of nature are the same in all inertial systems — Einstein.

3. Time is universal — the same for all — contra-Einstein.

It is assumed in the classical theory of relativity that postulate 2 applies not only to mechanical phenomena but to light transmission as well; that is, it is postulated that whenever beams are emitted from a source, the velocity of the beams is the same in all directions relative to the source — relative to the inertial system in which their source is at rest.

It is assumed also in accord with postulate 2 that when light is reflected in a mirror the velocity of the reflected ray equals the velocity of the incident ray relative to the mirror.

It follows from these assumptions that the velocity of light is not to be regarded as constant except in the system in which its source is at rest, and then only before reflection if the mirror is moving. In any system in which a source of light is in motion the velocity of the source is imparted to the beams.

It is assumed in accord with postulate 3 that events that are simultaneous in any inertial system are simultaneous in all inertial systems — contra Einstein.

It is assumed in accord with postulate 3 that events can occur in only one order. (It has been shown that in accord with the Einstein theory events A and B can occur in the order *A-B* in one system and in the order *B-A* in another system.)

It is assumed that the parallelogram law of the addition of vectors is valid. (Einstein admits this law is valid for force vectors but denies its validity for velocity vectors.)

---

* The classical theory of relativity presented here bears a close resemblance to the so-called emission theories of W. Ritz, O. M. Stewart, and J. J. Thompson. (See W. Pauli, *Theory of Relativity*, p. 7, or Richard C. Tolman, *Relativity, Thermodynamics, and Cosmology*, p. 16.)

It is assumed (contrary to Einstein) that the mass or inertia of a body is constant and proportional to the amount of matter in the body.

It is assumed that the kinetic energy of a body is in accord with the time-honored equation: $E_k = \frac{1}{2}mv^2$ not $(k - 1)m_0$, as claimed by Einstein.)

It is understood that mass (meaning matter) can be converted into energy in a nuclear reaction (but only in a nuclear reaction) and that the number of ergs of energy obtainable from m grams of matter is expressed by the equation $E = mc^2$.

It can be shown that this equation is not derived mathematically from the Einstein theory. It is only, as Van Name* calls it, "an attractive hypothesis," so far as the Einstein theory is concerned.

It is assumed that the law of the conservation of energy is valid.

It is assumed that in an equation such as $F = ma$ (force equals mass times acceleration) the term *mass* refers to quantity of matter only: whereas Einstein has been obliged in his theory to redefine "mass" to include kinetic energy, and the potential energy of compression, heat, etc.

Constant vs. relative time. We may distinguish between the classicist's concept of the universality of time and Einstein's concept of time as relative by saying merely that the classicist defines time by reference to a *single clock* which is postulated as having a constant rate; whereas Einstein defines time by reference to *many clocks*, any one of which is assumed by the theory to vary in its rate depending upon its motion relative to some inertial system.

Thus, the classicist will choose as his single clock either the earth in its daily rotation, or the earth in its yearly revolution, or possibly the vibration of some molecule, if its rate of vibration can be considered constant (at least under standard conditions). For centuries scientists have defined a second as $1/86,400$ of a 'day'.

Einstein on the other hand defines time as whatever any clock says — by which is meant that if the clocks at the two ends of a moving train read differently when the train is in any given position, Einstein says that the time is therefore different at the two ends of the train. And if, as he claims, the clocks on a moving train run more slowly than those on the ground, *time* on the train he says goes more slowly. As Einstein says (Relativity, p. 32) "Every reference body (coordinate system) has its own particular time."

*F. W. Van Name, *Modern Physics*, p. 82.

No violation of postulates. The concept of the universality of time as defined above does not in any way violate either the postulate of the relativity of motion, or of the uniform laws of nature, or the postulate that the velocity of light relative to the inertial system in which its source is at rest is (before reflection) a universal constant.

Defining time. The question might arise as to how to define the universal time at any given place in the universe. This might be done as follows in accord with the concept that the laws of nature are the same in all inertial systems and hence in any inertial system (such as that of an observatory) the velocity of light from a source at rest is c in all directions.

Let us say we wish to define time throughout the universe in terms of the rate and setting of the standard clock at the Naval Observatory at Washington. Let us say all the clocks in the universe are of identical construction and are regulated so that if any such clock were adjacent to the standard clock at Washington the two would tick off seconds in unison forever. All the clocks will then be defined as having the rate of 'universal time' and accordingly seconds as ticked off by all the clocks will be of the same duration by universal time. (It is assumed in accord with classical concepts that the motion of a clock has no effect upon its rate.) There then remains only the matter of defining the synchronisation of these clocks. This may be done as follows.

Let a single time signal be sent from the Naval Observatory at Washington, at an instant defined as being O by universal time. We may then say that at the instant the wave front of the signal has attained the radius c the time at every point on the wave front is defined to be time 1. At the instant the wave front has attained the radius $2c$ the time at every point on the wave front will be defined to be time 2, etc. At any instant at which the wave front has attained the radius nc (n being *any* number) the time at any point on the wave front will be defined as time n — i.e. n seconds.

Since the clocks tick off seconds of equal duration, as provided, we have merely to say that any clock in the universe which is so set as to read the time as just defined will register universal time as defined, and so all the clocks would be synchronized in accord with universal time as defined.

An important realization. It is important in this connection to realize that if the time officials on Mars decided to define time in accord with the standard clock at their own observatory assuming it to be one of the identically constructed and regulated clocks, they could do so in the same manner as prescribed above, sending out a signal to define zero' time by their standard clock. In that case Martian time would be just as universal as Washington time and a second would be of the same duration in both systems. The time systems would differ in no way except as to what was defined as zero time (in the same way that Chicago time differs from New York time). Zero time is arbitrary and can be assigned to any instant in a system of universal time.

However, because Mars is in motion relative to Washington, if the officials on Mars made the mistake of assuming that light signals from Washington had the same velocity c relative to Mars that they have relative to Washington, and if they attempted to define simultaneity on Mars in terms of the signals sent from Washington they would find that their definition of simultaneity was different from that on the Earth for the same reason that the observer on the train in Fig. 4-1 got a different simultaneity on the train from that on the ground (considering events D, E, F, and G as simultaneous) because of the mistake of thinking that beams X and Y arrived simultaneously at —3 and +3 of the train.

But, as indicated above, if the Martians sent out their own time signal which had the velocity c in all directions relative to Mars, their definition of simultaneity would be exactly the same as that of the Earth.

Hence we see that if we can rid ourselves of the conviction that the velocity of all beams is the same in all inertial systems, there is no problem about defining universal time.

Universal time in accord with the principle of relativity. The only need Einstein had to give up the concept of the universality of time was occasioned by his effort to demonstrate mathematically his postulate of the constant velocity of light, according to which in any inertial system the velocity of all beams is c whether the source is at rest in the system or not.

But it is clear that if we give up that postulate and substitute the postulate that in any inertial system the velocity of all beams whose source is at rest in that system is c, we find this to be quite in accord with the postulate of relativity.

And since there is therefore no need to give up the concept of the universality of time, we may adhere to it — and avoid all the irrational concepts and contradictions of the Einstein theory, and yet retain its fundamental concept that the laws of nature are the same in all inertial systems.

A classical theory of absolutity. If subsequent experiment should demonstrate quite conclusively that there is an ether relative to which the velocity of unreflected light and electromagnetic waves is constant, we may need to adopt what might be called a classical theory of absolutity, based upon postulates such as the following.

1. There is an ether with respect to which any velocity may be regarded as absolute velocity — the ether being regarded as at absolute rest.

2. The velocity of unreflected light is constant relative to the ether only.

3. The mechanical laws of nature are the same in all inertial systems.

4. The velocity of reflection equals the velocity of incidence relative to the mirror.

5. Time is universal—the flow of time is the same everywhere.

6. The parallelogram law of the addition of velocity vectors is valid.

7. Kinetic energy $= \frac{1}{2}mv^2$.

8. Mass is constant.

An impossible reconciliation. It has been shown (p. 16) that so far as the principle of relativity is concerned there was no need for the postulate of the constant velocity of light in the first place. And it is seen (p. 96) that the reason given by Einstein himself for the postulate turned out to be invalid and therefore not requiring the postulate after all. This leaves only one further possible need for the postulate and that is to harmonize the evidence of binary stars (which seem to uphold the ether theory) with the evidence of the Michelson-Morley and Kennedy-Thorndike experiments (which upheld the source theory).

But let us remember that the ether theory is based upon a concept that there is a *unique frame of reference* in which and only in which the velocity of light is constant. But the basic concept of the Einstein theory of relativity is that there is *no unique frame of reference* such as an ether would of necessity constitute. Under no circumstances, therefore, can the Einstein theory presume to harmonize evidence upholding the ether theory with evidence upholding the source theory by presuming to harmonize the ether and source theories.

If we are to adhere to the principle of relativity, according to which there is no unique frame of reference and the laws of nature are the same in all inertial systems, this means that we adhere to the concept that when there is a source of light at rest in a system S the light from that source will have a constant velocity in that system, and that if the source is moving with velocity v in the system the motion of the source will be imparted to its beams so that the velocity of its beams will vary from $c - v$ to $c + v$ according to direction.

A challenge. If we adhere to the principle of relativity, therefore, the challenge remains to young phyicists and astronomers to solve the problem of the binary stars, in terms of that concept — not in terms of any unique frame of reference. And let us no longer pretend that the solution requires the acceptance of a theory which has as a consequence that an infinite series of events may be considered under certain circumstances as constituting a single instant!

Summary of Section 9. Section 9 :—➤
(1) presents a classicial theory of relativity;
(2) distinguishes between universal and relative time;
(3) defines universal time;
(4) presents a 'classical theory of absolutity;
(5) offers a challenge to young scientists.

10. WHY THE THEORY PERSISTS

Why the persistence of the Einstein theory? Since it has been shown in this booklet that no theory can be valid if it is an impossible theory, no matter how well it seems to have been confirmed; and since it has been shown that the Einstein theory is an impossible theory because it has contradictory consequences, the question may well arise: Why does the Einstein theory persist? The following may be some of the reasons.

Belief in its confirmation It appears to be generally believed that the Einstein theory has been amply confirmed — particularly by the Fizeau experiment and the many instances in which a charged particle accelerated in an electric field appears to increase in mass in accord with the prediction of the Einstein theory.

We have seen, however, that the seeming confirmation of the theory by the Fizeau experiment was based upon mistaken reasoning by Einstein, and the behavior of charged particles does not confirm the theory because it can be explained in terms of increased energy, there being no experimental fact showing that an ordinary uncharged body would acquire an increment of mass by virtue of mere motion relative to some inertial system. Indeed, it is shown graphically that mere relative motion cannot increase mass.

It would appear, therefore, that the strong belief in the theory results in part from the erroneous belief that the theory has been amply confirmed by the behavior of highspeed particles.

Misconception regarding confirmation. It appears to be generally considered that if a consequence of the Einstein theory, such as the increase in mass with increase in velocity, is confirmed, the theory itself is confirmed. This is not so. It is well known in logic that the confirmation of a consequence does not confirm the antecedent.

For example, a theory was once propounded that we live on the inside of a hollow sphere. A consequence of that theory would be that we could 'circumnavigate the globe'. We have circumnavigated the globe, thus confirming the consequence of the theory. Does that confirm the theory? Obviously not! Hence we must remember that the Einstein theory is not confirmed by the confirmation of any of its consequences, such as the mass-velocity relation.

The only way the theory could be considered as confirmed would be by the actual measurement of the velocity relative to the earth of beams from a source in motion relative to the earth. This has never been done directly; hence we may say that the Einstein theory has never been confirmed.

Belief in the theory may rest on the erroneous assumption that it has been confirmed.

Mistaken interpretation of experiment. It is often stated that the Einstein theory is based upon the null result of the Michelson-Morley experiment, as if this result demonstrated that any observer would find all beams from all sources to have a constant velocity relative to him. The Einstein theory is regarded then as a theory to explain how all beams from all sources could have a constant velocity relative to any observer.

Let us remember, however, that in the Michelson-Morley experiment the source of light and the observer were both stationary on the earth, and hence that the most that the null result could demonstrate is that if the observer is *moving with the source* he will find the velocities of beams from that source to be constant. It could not demonstrate that *any observer* (moving relative to the source) would find beams from that source to have a constant velocity relative to him.

It would appear, therefore, that the theory was based upon a mistaken interpretation of the Michelson-Morley experiment, and that so far as that experiment is concerned there was no reason for the Einstein theory in the first place.

Failure to consider important criteria. It has been pointed out that there are three criteria of the acceptability of a theory, these being:

(1) Is it a rational theory?

(2) Is it a possible theory?

(3) Does it accord with experiment and observation?

It would appear that the theory has been evaluated entirely on the basis of the third criterion; that is, with little or no regard as to whether it is rational or possible.

Contradictions explained away. It is true that Einsteinists recognize certain contradictions and 'paradoxes' in the theory, but when one is firmly convinced that it has been confirmed beyond question there is a tendency to try to explain away the contradictions by recourse to the appearance interpretation, etc. — not realizing that such efforts merely lead to further contradictions, as has been shown.

Contradictions not discovered. It is customary to treat the Einstein theory is purely mathematical. The mathematics of the theory completely obscures the contradictions pointed out in this booklet. It is not customary to analyze the theory graphically in the manner of this booklet — a method that brings out the contradictions clearly. It may be that for these reasons the contradictions of the theory have gone unrecognized.

Disproof of the fundamental postulate. It has been shown in this booklet that when a spectroscope moves relative to a source of light the spectrum of the light is displaced from its normal position, indicating a change of frequency of the reception of the light by the spectroscope, since the wavelength of the light from a stationary source is in no way affected by the motion of the spectroscope. Everyone knows that velocity equals wavelength multiplied by frequency. But it appears to be wholly overlooked that the changing frequency with which waves of a constant length are received by a spectroscope (as indicated by a shift of a spectrum) indicates a change of velocity of the light relative to the spectroscope — disproving the fundamental postulate of the Einstein theory: that the velocity of light is constant.

It appears not to be realized that the phenomenon of the aberration of starlight contradicts the Einstein postulate of the constant velocity of light.

Prestige. The theory has been in existance so long without its contradictions being pointed out that by now it has acquired a tremendous prestige — so great that it has become heresy to doubt it.

Other possible reasons could be given.

The challenge. Progress in science is not made by the mere disproving of a theory. But progress in a science can be prevented by the retention of an invalid theory which presumes to solve a problem which is in fact unsolved.

The need to refute the Einstein theory is only to clear the way for progress. By claiming to demonstrate how the velocity of light can be constant relative to the cosmos and relative to its source and relative to any observer, the theory has blinded us to the problem which is just as present and just as urgent now as it was in the days of Michelson and Morley: Is the velocity of a source of light imparted to its beams or not? Hence the challenge to young scientists!

SUPPLEMENT 1

SOURCE THEORY VS. ETHER THEORY

Graphic representation. The difference between the consequences of the two theories is illustrated in Fig. S-1. Each graph is a space-time graph comparable to Fig. 2-1, representing the motion of a platform in space past a row of stars. In each case it is supposed that a source of light is situated at the 0 point of the platform — moving with it — sending out two beams each second, one to the right and one to the left. The motion of the first pair of beams is represented by the space-time lines *AE* and *AF,* the next pair by the lines *BG* and *BH,* etc.

Graph (*a*) shows that, according to the ether theory, even though the source is moving relative to the stars (and ether) the beams have equal velocities relative to the stars (and ether), each beam moving one unit distance per second relative to the stars. (The first pair of beams reaching stars —3 and 3 in 3 seconds.)

Graph (*b*) shows that, according to the source theory, (with the source moving uniformly in a straight line) the beams of each pair reach equal distances from the source in one second. (The first pair of beams reach points —3 and 3 on the platform in 3 seconds.)

Fourth contradiction. In each graph the distances *EG, GI,* and *ID* represents the wavelengths of the light emitted to the left and the dis· tances *DJ, JH,* and *HF* represent the wavelengths of the light emitted to the right. Comparing these distances we see that according to the source theory (graph *b*) the wavelengths are equal in the two directions; whereas, according to the ether theory (graph a) the wavelengths on the left are longer and those on the right are shorter. We might say that the wavelengths are shortest 'ahead' of the moving source and longest 'behind' the moving source.

Wavelengths cannot be both of constant length and of different lengths; hence we have a fourth way in which the ether theory and source theory are incompatible.

A fifth contradiction. In each group the dotted semicircles represent the spherical wavefronts emitted successively at the several instants. The semicircles in graph (*b*) show that according to the source theory the successive wavefronts at instant 3 are concentric. It can be shown similarly that at *any* instant all the wavefronts from a uniformly moving source are concentric. Whereas, the semicircles in graph (*a*) show that according to the ether theory the successive wavefronts are

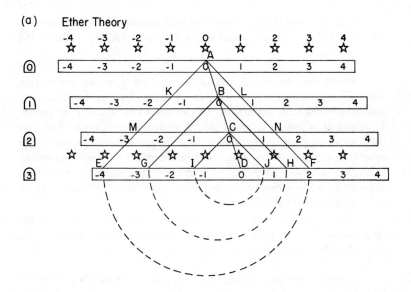

(a) Ether Theory

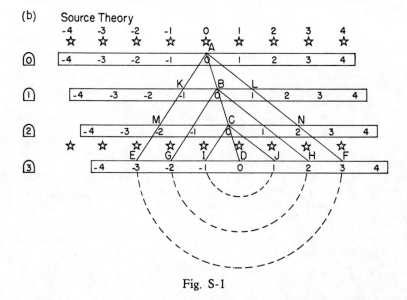

(b) Source Theory

Fig. S-1

not concentric. The center of each wavefront is further forward than that of the preceding wavefront.

Successive wavefronts cannot be both concentric and not concentric. Hence this difference constitutes a fifth contradiction between the two theories.

A sixth contradiction. It can be shown that if we are considering not successive wavefronts emitted at successive instants but successive positions of the same wavefront (as represented by K and L at instant 1, M and N at instant 2, and E and F at instant 3) we will find that these successive positions of a wavefront are concentric according to the ether theory (their center being fixed in the ether); whereas, according to the source theory they will be eccentric. That is, as the wavefront expands its center moves with the source — provided the source moves uniformly in a straight line.

The center of an expanding wavefront cannot remain fixed in the ether and at the same time move forward with the source; hence a sixth contradiction between the ether theory and source theory.

Contrary concepts. We now have six reasons for deciding definitely that the velocities of the beams from a given source moving in the ether cannot be equal both relative to the ether and relative to their source.

SUPPLEMENT 2

EVIDENCE OF THE SPECTROSCOPE

An attempt to refute the reasoning. An attempt has been made to refute the reasoning (p 10) in disproof of the postulate by recourse to Einstein's concepts of the 'behavior of measuring rods and clocks in motion' (see Chapter XII in his *Relativity*), claiming that as the spectroscope moves toward the source of light, the wavelengths of light, as received by the spectroscope are shorter than when the spectroscope is stationary relative to the source, and that a clock moving with the spectroscope (by which frequency would be measured) would run more slowly than when at rest; and that taking these effects into account we would find that the shift of the spectrum of the light did not indicate a change in the velocity of the light relative to the spectroscope. Let us *see* whether this is so .

According to Einstein a clock moving with the spectroscope would run only $\sqrt{(1 - v^2/c^2)}$ as fast as when it is stationary — v representing the velocity of the spectroscope relative to the source of light. How much effect is this?

Let us say that by virtue of the orbital motion of the earth the spectroscope approaches the source of light with the velocity $v = 30$ km. per sec. The velocity of light is 300,000 km. per sec.; hence $v = c/10,000$, and $\sqrt{(1 - v^2/c^2)} = 0.999,999,995$. So according to Einstein the rate of the hypothetical spectroscope clock would be reduced by only 0.000,000,005, a completely negligible amount.

Similarly it can be shown that if the wavelengths of the light were reduced to $\sqrt{(1 - v^2/c^2)}$ in accord with Einstein, they would be reduced only 0.000,000,005 — also a completely negligible amount.

Hence the alleged shortening of the wavelengths of the light as received by the spectroscope in motion and the alleged slowing of the hypothetical spectroscope clock, even if true, could not appreciably affect the statement that if the orbital motion of the earth caused the spectroscope to approach a star with the velocity of 30 km. per sec., the displacement of the spectrum of the starlight would show definitely that the frequency of the light, as received by the spectroscope had been increased by 1/10,000, thereby indicating that the velocity of the light relative to the spectroscope had been increased by 1/10,000.

There is no way by which Einstein's alleged 'behavior of measuring rods and clocks in motion' can explain away the evidence of the spectroscope that the velocity of light is relative — not constant.

Spectroscope with diffraction grating. When light of different colors enters a grating spectroscope the dispersion of colors is caused theoretically by differences in wavelength of the colors. In view of this it has been said that the shift of the spectrum when the spectroscope approaches a source of light is proof that the relative motion of the spectroscope alters the wavelength of the light.

But dispersion of colors of light when the source and spectroscope are at relative rest is one phenomenon and a shift of the spectrum when there is relative motion between spectroscope and source is another phenomenon. In the latter case it is conceivable that a change of velocity of the light relative to the spectroscope could cause the shift of the spectrum.

No change of wavelength resulting from relative motion. Let us say a motor boat has created a train of waves on a lake. Let us say some birds are skimming back and forth over the waves. Each bird is an object in motion relative to the waves. Can the birds flying toward the oncoming waves reduce the distance between crests; and can the birds flying in the opposite direction increase the distance between crests? The classicist says that relative motion of the birds cannot possibly affect the distance between crests (wavelengths) of the waves.

If the mere motion of an object relative to a train of waves could affect the wavelength of the waves, then every time a train of waves is emitted by a source of light the wavelengths of that train of waves would be affected by the relative motion of every moving object in the universe — meteors, comets, satellites, birds, flies, and dust particles — some shortening the wavelengths and some increasing them.

In that case every bird flying toward a source of light would have to shorten the wavelengths exactly in inverse proportion to the increase in the frequency of reception of the waves by the bird — so that frequency times wavelength would remain constant, according to Einstein. And if the waves came from a distant star would the relative motion of the bird (or even the spectroscope) shorten the wavelengths all the way back to the star — and then lengthen them if the bird or spectroscope moved away from the star?

An ether? It is important to remember that the wavelength of beams from a given source can be different in different directions only if there is a unique frame of reference (such as an ether) and if the velocity of light is constant relative to this unique frame of reference only, and the source of light is in motion relative to this unique frame of reference. And the moment one adopts this concept of the unique frame of reference he repudiates the Einstein theory which denies the existence of any unique frame of reference.

Indeed, there may be an ether, but even if there is, the wavelength of light from a star is unaffected by the motion of birds, meteors, or spectroscopes.

Light velocity not constant. The classicist repeats, therefore, that the motion of a spectroscope relative to a train of waves cannot change their wavelength. Hence when the spectroscope indicates a change of frequency of reception of the waves (by a shift of the spectrum) it thereby indicates a change in the velocity of the waves relative to the spectroscope. This disproves the Einstein postulate of the 'constant velocity of light'.

SUPPLEMENT 3

POSTULATE NOT NEEDED

Origin of theory based upon mistaken concept. We have seen already that Einstein's postulate of the 'constant velocity of light' appears to have been based upon faulty reasoning regarding the significance of the Michelson-Morley null result. A careful reading of Einstein's *Relativity* reveals additional faulty reasoning which Einstein himself presents as showing the need for his postulate of the 'constant velocity of light'. Let us review this reasoning.

In Chapter VII Einstein considers the velocity of a beam of light emitted from a source on the ground as measured by an observer on a moving train. The beam moves in the same direction as the train and is represented by the space-time line AC in Fig. S-3. We will consider Einstein's reasoning in the light of this figure.

Einstein tells us (p. 22) that according to the classical law of the addition of velocities the velocity W of this beam relative to the train is $c - v$ with v representing the velocity of the train. In Fig. S-3 $v = c/3$; hence $c - v = 2c/3$, which is the same as 2 units in 3 seconds; and we see that in the figure beam AC moves 2 units along the train in 3 seconds. Hence we can agree with Einstein so far.

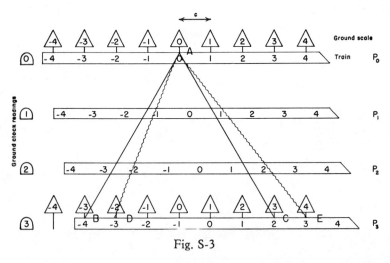

Fig. S-3

He tells us (p. 23) that according to his principle of relativity the law of the transmission of light must be the same for the train as for the ground. This means that beams emitted from a source on the ground will have the velocity c relative to the ground (as represented by beams AB and AC) and beams emitted from a source on the train as a second reference body will have the velocity c relative to the train (as represented by beams AD and AE).* We can agree also with Einstein's second statement.

But he has just told us (top of p. 23) that 'this result'—referring to the velocity of beam AC being $c - v$, or $2c/3$ in accord with the classical law of the addition of velocities—is "in conflict with the principle of relativity."

He is saying, in effect, that because (according to the principle of relativity) beams AD and AE (whose source is on the train) have velocities c relative to the train, it is therefore impossible for beam AC (whose source is on the ground) to have the velocity $2c/3$ relative to the train.

This, of course, is not true. There is no conflict here. Beams AD and AE do have the velocity c relative to the train and beam AC, having its source on the ground and having the velocity c relative to ground in accord with the principle of relativity, *does* have the velocity $2c/3$ relative to the train, as the figure plainly shows.

But seemingly because Einstein believed there was a conflict between the principle of relativity and the classical law of the addition (and subtraction) of velocities, he renounced the latter and decided that in accord with the principle of relativity the velocity of beam AC must be c both relative to the ground and relative to the train. Hence his postulate of the 'constant velocity of light'.

Postulate not needed. Thus we see that the postulate of the constant velocity of light — the special feature of the Einstein theory of relativity — was based on mistaken reasoning, so was not needed in the first place.

*So far as the transmission of light is concerned, the 'principle of relativity' is represented by the 'source theory' as defined herein.

FURTHER CONTRADICTIONS IN THE THEORY

A further contradiction in the Einstein theory. It can be shown that a second contradiction in the Einstein theory arises in the application of the Einstein transformation equations in the case of trains moving in opposite directions relative to the ground with a source of light on each train. Here is how.

The graphs of Fig. S-4 represent trains moving relative to a stationary platform — train T moving to the left in graph (a) and train R moving to the right in graph (b). At instant i_o beams X and Y are emitted from a source at the origin of train T and beams X' and Y' are emitted from a source at the origin of train R.

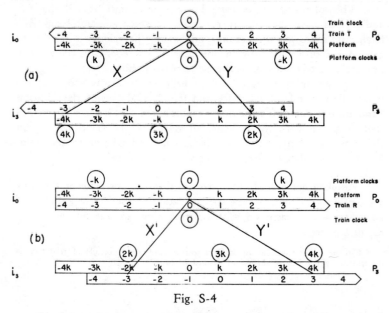

Fig. S-4

Now in order to make the velocities of beams X and Y come out equal relative to the platform, the theory assumes that the scale units on the platform corresponding to those on the train will be as shown — k units on the platform equaling 1 unit on the train, and that when the train is in any given position relative to the platform the platform clocks all read differently — each reading later than those to the right of it — as shown by the clocks reading $4k$, $3k$, and $2k$ in graph (a), in order to presume that the observer on the platform will find by the two-clock method that beam X moved $4k$ units in $4k$ seconds and that beam Y moved $2k$ units in $2k$ seconds — each moving 1 unit per second.

(In this case we are required by the theory to regard the platform as the 'moving' system, represented by x' and t' of the transformation equations. Otherwise the platform clocks would all read 3 at instant i_3 and the velocities of the beams relative to the platform would come out 4 units in 3 seconds and 2 units in 3 seconds, contradicting the postulate.)

On the other hand, to make the velocities of beams X' and Y' come out equal relative to the platform, the theory assumes that k units on the platform equal 1 unit on train R and that when train R is in any given position relative to the platform, the platform clocks all read differently, but in this case each reading later than those to the *left* of it, as shown by the clock readings $2k$, $3k$, and $4k$ in graph (b), in order to presume that the observer on the platform will find that beam X' moved $2k$ units in $2k$ seconds and that beam Y' moved $4k$ units in $4k$ seconds (using the two-clock method, of course), or 1 unit per second for each beam.

This means that to make the velocities of beams X and Y come out equal relative to the platform and at the same time make the velocities of beams X' and Y' come out equal relative to the platform, the platform clocks would have to be out of synchronism as in graph (a), that is, with the clock readings increasing to the *left*, and at the same time out of synchronism as in graph (b), that is, with the clock readings increasing to the *right*.

The contradiction. Obviously the platform clocks could not be out of synchronism in both these opposite ways at the same time. This contradiction, then, also invalidates the theory.

Incompatible concepts. As was said in Section 1, it is customary in physics texts to say, "The velocity of light$_3$ is independent of the motion of *its* source."* It was shown that this statement can be interpreted in accord with the source theory if it is read: The velocity of light *relative to its source* is independent of the motion of its source. It can be interpreted also in accord with the ether theory if it is read: The velocity of light *relative to the cosmos* is independent of the motion of its source relative to the cosmos.

Indeed, Einstein tells us that De Sitter was able to show that "the velocity of propagation of light cannot depend on the velocity of mo-

* See Eisberg, Modern Physics, p. 16.

tion of the body emitting the light." He makes it clear that he is thinking of the velocity of light "in space". (*Relativity*, p. 21.) He is telling
us, therefore, that De Sitter showed that the velocity of light in space is
independent of the motion of its source in space. This is the ether theory!

It is common for Einsteinists to think of the Einstein theory as
one which harmonizes or combines the ether theory and the source
theory. Thus, Tolman* speaks repeatedly of "combining the principles" of the ether theory and Einstein's first postulate, with which the
source theory is in strict accord as has been amply shown.

To the extent, therefore, to which the Einstein theory is regarded
as reconciling the ether and source theories, the classicist considers it invalid because six ways were shown in which the ether theory and source
theory were incompatible and mutually contradictory.

The meaning of symbols. The inherent contradiction in the Einstein
theory can be shown in other terms. Thus, if we are dealing with two
given inertial systems it is customary in accord with the theory to
regard one of the systems as 'at rest' and the other 'in motion'. It is
customary also to designate the 'at-rest' system as system S and the
'in-motion' system as system S'. In that case it is customary to regard
the symbols x and t of the transformation equations (see page 32) as
denoting measurements of distance and time for a given event, made in
system S, and to regard the symbols x' and t' as denoting measurements
of distance and time for the same event, made in system S'. It is to be
clearly understood that as used in the transformation equations the
symbols x and t represent measurements made by observers in system S
reading the scale and clocks of system S; and that the symbols x' and t'
represent measurements made by observers in system S' reading the
scale and clocks of system S'. (For the purpose of measuring the velocity of light relative to his system an observer need *never read the
scale or clocks of another system*.)**

'At rest' or 'in motion'. This being the case, it follows from the
Einstein theory that if we merely consider train T as the 'at-rest' system (and call it system S) and train R the 'in-motion' system (system

*Relativity, Thermodynamics, and Cosmology, p. 15.

****The appearance interpretation.** It is contended by some Einsteinists that in the
Einstein transformation equations the symbols x' and t' refer merely to the scale reading and clock reading of an event that the observer in system S *thinks* the observer
in system S' would obtain for that event. If that were true all we could say for the
Einstein theory as demonstrating the constant velocity of light is that if a source of
light is at rest on the ground and the observer on the ground found the velocities of
beams from that source to be equal, he might *think* that an observer on the train
reading the train scale and train clocks would find the velocities of those beams equal
relative to the train also. That would demonstrate nothing, of course, as to what the
observer *on the train* would find regarding the velocities of those beams.

100

S') the transformation equations indicate that when the 0 mark of train R coincides with the 1 mark of train T, the clocks on the two trains will read as shown in graph (a) of Fig. 5-2 — showing the train T clocks to be in synchronism in the sense of all reading the same and the train R clocks out of synchronism in the sense of all reading differently when the trains are in a single relative position. Indeed, in this case, for *any* relative position of the two trains the T clocks are in synchronism and the R clocks out of synchronism in the above sense.

On the other hand we have merely to consider train R as the 'at rest' system (system S) and train T the 'in-motion' system (system S') and the transformation equations indicate that when the 0 mark of train T coincides with the —1 mark of train R, the clocks on the two trains will read as shown in graph (b) — showing that the train R clocks are in synchronism and the train T clocks out of synchronism in the above sense. Indeed in this case also, for *any* relative position of the two trains the R clocks are in synchronism and the train T clocks out of synchronism.

The contradiction .Now, as has been said, the essence of the Einstein 'principle of relativity' is that each of the two trains is equally in motion relative to the other. This means that according to the theory it is true both that train T is 'in motion' (and train R 'at rest') and that train R is 'in motion' (and train T 'at rest'). This means in turn that according to the theory when the trains are in any given relative position* it is true both (1) that the clocks on train T are in synchronism and those on train R are out of synchronism and (2) that the clocks on train R are in synchronism and those on train T are out of synchronism. Of course, this is an impossibility; and the classicist considers this impossibility to render the theory an impossible theory.

*A 'given relative position' of the trains would be one in which let us say the —1 mark of the R scale coincides with the 1 mark of the T scale. At this point of coincidence both t and t' will equal $k/(k-1)$ according to the theory.

101

SUPPLEMENT 5
A DEVICE TO ILLUSTRATE THE ABERRATION OF STARLIGHT
AND DISPROVE THE EINSTEIN POSTULATE
(See p. 8)

Directions for making the device. The device is to consist of two parts, a 'trough' and a 'slide' — the motion of the slide in the trough to represent the motion of a telescope relative to the cosmos.

1. With semi-transparent paper laid over the accompanying drawing trace the drawing accurately, omitting the part labeled 'End view of trough'.

(If appropriate, in lieu of tracing the drawing, the leaf of the booklet containing the drawing may be removed and the drawing itself used.)

2. Cut out the upper rectangle and fold the edges up on the dotted lines to form the *trough,* as shown by the end view.

3. Cut out the lower rectangle (with flap) to form the *slide.*

4. With a razor blade cut along the adjacent parallel lines within the telescope to form a slot along its center line.

Directions for use of the device. As explained on page 8, the line *AB* in the trough represents a portion of the path of a beam from a star decending vertically in the cosmos. The drawing on the slide represents a telescope with which the star is being seen. Motion of the slide in the trough represents the horizontal motion of the observatory in the cosmos. Because of this motion the telescope must be held at a slant so that the beam can traverse the telescope.

1. Place the slide in the trough so that point *A* of the telescope coincides with point *A* of the vertical path.

2. Hold the trough with the left hand and with the right hand move the slide to the right. Repeat this motion of the slide and watch the 'beam' (black spot) move down the center line of the telescope. (It also moves down the vertical path.)

3. Note that the 'beam' begins its motion down path *AC* in the telescope at the same instant (instant 0) that it begins its motion down path *AB* relative to the cosmos. Note also that the 'beam' arrives at point *C* of the telescope at the same instant (instant 1) that it arrives at point *B* of the vertical path.

4. Note that path *AC* is longer than path *AB*. Since the travel time is identical in the two paths it follows that the velocity of the beam along path *AC* is greater than its velocity along path *AB*. This shows that a beam can have one velocity relative to the cosmos and another velocity relative to a telescope moving in the cosmos.

5. This contradicts the literal interpretation of the statement: "The velocity of light *is* a universal constant."

A DEVISE TO DEMONSTRATE RELATIVE MOTION

Trough

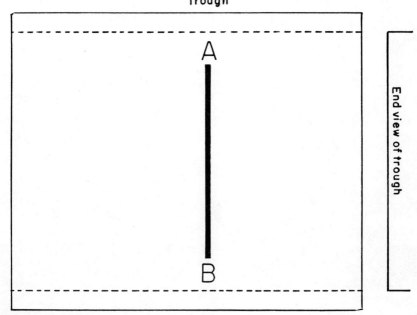

Slide

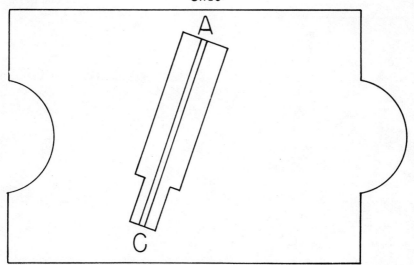

With razor blade make a narrow slot AC

APPENDIX

THE GENERAL THEORY OF RELATIVITY

1a. THE PRINCIPLE OF EQUIVALENCE

The general theory. After proposing in 1905 the theory of relativity with which this booklet has dealt, Einstein set forth in 1916 an extension of that theory which he called the General Theory of Relativity. The original theory is therefore commonly referred to as the special theory of relativity.

The appendix. The first and second editions of this booklet contained no discussion of the general theory. However, in the interest of completeness it has seemed desirable in this third edition to include a brief treatment of the general theory. Hence the addition of this appendix.

Postulates of the general theory. Since the general theory is an extension of the special theory we may consider that the postulates of the special theory are included among those of the general theory. In the general theory the postulate of the relativity of uniform motion has been extended to include the relativity of non-uniform motion. The principal postulate of the general theory Einstein calls the *principle of equivalence.*

Deductions from the general theory. From the postulates of the special and general theories Einstein has deduced, or presumes to have deduced, additional concepts, among which are
the curvature of light rays in a gravitational field,
the non-Euclidean world,
the four-dimensional space-time continuum, and
the curvature of space.

Purpose of the appendix. The purpose of this appendix is to examine and evaluate the postulates of the general theory and the deductions therefrom.

It will be found that the curvature of light rays in a gravitational field is not a true deduction from the general theory and can be accounted for in terms of classical concepts. However, the concepts of the non-Euclidean world, the four-dimensional space-time continuum, and the curvature of space are Einsteinian and not in accord with classical concepts.

The purpose of this section is to examine the so-called principle of equivalence. The section will show the similarity that Einstein has pointed out between two coordinate systems, one of which is in uniform acceleration and the other in a gravitational field. It is from this similarity that Einstein deduces his principle of equivalence.

Non-uniform motion relative. Einstein says (Einstein and Infeld, *The Evolution of Physics*, p. 224), "Could we build a relativist physics valid in all coordinate systems; a physics in which there would be no place for absolute, but only for relative motion? This is indeed possible?" He says (p. 235) that "there is nothing absolute in the non-uniform motion."

The neo-relativist (believer in the classical theory of relativity proposed in this booklet) agrees that if one body or system is in straight-line acceleration relative to another we may consider that the second body or system is equally in acceleration relative to the first.

Also it can be agreed that each of the two stars of a binary system or each of the two balls of the governor of a steam engine is equally in revolution around the other.

There is nothing about these concepts of the relativity of systems in straight-line acceleration or in mutual revolution that in any way conflicts with the classicist concept of the universality of time, simultaneity, and sequence.

However, it cannot be admitted that all motion is relative only— even all uniform motion. Thus a rotating phonograph record may be regarded as in uniform motion but by no stretch of the imagination could we consider that when the record is being played the record is stationary and the whole universe is rotating around it.

Presuming that Einstein would agree to this statement we may say that so far as the relativity of accelerated motion is concerned the general theory is not differentiated from the classical theory of relativity.

The principle of equivalence. As has been indicated, the principal postulate of the general theory of relativity is the so-called *principle of equivalence*. This principle is based upon a certain similarity, which Einstein points out, between the behavior of bodies in a system (chest) that is in uniform acceleration and the behavior of bodies in a gravitational field. Let us see what that similarity is and then consider the principle of equivalence that Einstein has based upon it.

The accelerated chest. Einstein tells us (*Relativity* p. 78) to imagine a large portion of empty space far removed from stars so that it is free from gravitation. He then asks us to imagine a spacious chest

106

resembling a room with an observer inside, and to imagine that by means of a rope attached to the top of the chest, the chest is being accelerated upward uniformly. He then explains that the experience of the observer inside the chest will be such that "the man in the chest will thus come to the conclusion that he and the chest are in a gravitational field." (p. 79).

Common experience. We may not have given thought to the similarity between a system in acceleration and a gravitational field but the similarity is a matter of common knowledge. We are all familiar with the fact that if we step into an elevator and it is lifted, we feel 'heavier' during the brief interval in which the elevator is being accelerated, as if the force of gravity became stronger during that interval. Those who have ridden in a roller coaster have experienced the sudden feeling of heaviness caused by the coaster going into an upward curve — a form of acceleration.

These then are two ways in which we are already familiar with the similarity between a system in acceleration and gravitational field.

Cause of the similarity. The reason the observer in the accelerated chest in empty space could not tell whether the chest was in acceleration or stationary in a gravitational field is that the laws of mechanics would be approximately the same in both cases.

Falling bodies. We know that in a room on earth a body dropped from rest will fall to the floor with an accelerated motion. If the force of gravity were considerably less than its actual force at the surface of the earth, we might find, for example, that a body would fall 1 foot in the first second, 3 feet in the second second, 5 feet in the third second, etc.

However, if we were in a room in empty space that is under uniform acceleration of one foot per second, not only would a force be required to accelerate the room upward, but also a force would be required upon every object in the room to accelerate it with the room. So, if we were holding a ball in the accelerated room we would have to exert an upward pressure upon it to keep it in acceleration — even in the absence of gravity — and this upward pressure would cause us to feel as though we were merely holding up the ball against a force of gravity.

If we released the ball it would cease to be accelerated. If the velocity of the ball relative to the cosmos at the instant of its release happened to be 100 feet per second, the ball, in the absence of gravity, would thereafter move upward in space at the uniform velocity of 100 feet per second. However, during the first second after the release the room in acceleration would move 101 feet upward in space, thus leaving the ball 1 foot behind, and making it appear that the ball had 'fallen' 1 foot. During the next second the room in acceleration would move upward 103 feet in space, whereas the ball would move only another 100 feet, thus leaving the ball 3 feet further behind and making it appear that the ball had 'fallen' another 3 feet. During the next second the room would move 105 feet, leaving the ball 5 feet further behind making it appear that the ball had 'fallen' an additional 5 feet that second, etc. This could cause the body to 'fall' in a room in eccleration in the absence of gravity exactly as it would in a weak gravitational field in which the force of gravity caused an acceleration in the manner described.

Limitation of the similarity. According to Einstein's principle of equivalence an observer in a room accelerated uniformly upward in the absence of gravity could not detect any difference between the downward force of inertia of material bodies in the room and a corresponding force of gravity. This does not mean, as we find Einstein in effect maintaining, that such a downward force of inertia *is* a force of gravity, or that any real force of gravity, as we know it, is generated by acceleration.

The differences. It may be seen that there are several differences in character between a true gravitational field and a simulated gravitational field produced in a system in uniform acceleration.

The most obvious difference perhaps is that a body in a gravitational field may be at rest relative to an inertial system (the field) whereas a body in acceleration cannot be at rest relative to any inertial system. (A body that is in acceleration in a straight line in any one inertial system is of necessity in the same acceleration in any other inertial system.)

A second difference is that the force of gravity is always centripetal — that is, acting toward a center — the center of the gravitational body; whereas in the case of the accelerated room the forces of inertia that simulate gravity act not toward a center but in parallel directions.

We know, of course, that a body that is in uniform revolution about a center is in one form of acceleration and Einstein often refers to this sort of acceleration, speaking of an observer situated on the edge of a rotating disc. However, we must realize that in the case of this form of acceleration the force that simulates gravity is a *centrifugal* force — one directed outward from the center and hence in this sense just the opposite of a true gravitational force.

Oddly enough, Einstein recognizes this difference, but in his effort to make it appear that gravity and the effect of acceleration are exactly equivalent — as he must for the purposes of his general theory — he says, after pointing out this difference (*Relativity* p. 94), "But since the observer believes in the general theory of relativity, this does not disturb him." He says that the observer "is quite in the right" when he believes in the principle of equivalence.

This makes it appear that the validity of the principle of equivalence depends upon one's belief in the general theory of relativity. It is so if you believe it is so!

A third difference is concerned with the extent to which acceleration can be carried. Thus, if a body were released in a chest that is in acceleration upward in empty space as Einstein suggests, so that the body 'fell' relative to the chest, we might think of the chest as having an opening in its floor which allowed the body to continue its 'fall' through the opening and out of the chest. In such a case the body could continue to 'fall' relative to the chest indefinitely. On the other hand, if a body is actually falling in a gravitational field it is falling toward the heavenly body that is the cause of the gravitation; and sooner or later the body must reach the 'ground' and cease falling. That is, a body in a gravitational field cannot fall indefinitely as it could relative to an accelerating chest.

A fourth difference is that as a body falls in a true gravitational field the force of gravity on it becomes greater and greater because of Newton's law that the force of attraction between two bodies is inversely proportional to the square of the distance between their centers, and consequently as that distance decreases the force of gravity increases and hence the acceleration increases; whereas in the case of the body that 'fell' through the opening in the floor of the chest in acceleration, there is no change in the rate of acceleration of the body relative to the chest. It will be well to bear in mind, therefore, that although an observer in a hypothetical accelerated chest might not be able to *detect* any difference between the simulated gravitational field and a real one, there are real differences nevertheless.

A principle of similarity. In the light of the above considerations, if we wish to be precise, we might state the following 'principle of similarity' between a reference system in acceleration and a gravitational field:

A body that is in a reference system in uniform acceleration, free from gravitation, behaves in certain respects *as if it were in a gravitational field.*

Einstein's statement of the principle of equivalence. Einstein appears to have stated his principle of equivalence most clearly as follows: "Bodies in a gravitational field behave as in the absence of a gravitational field if, in the latter case, the system of reference used is a uniformly accelerated coordinate system (instead of an inertial system)." (Einstein: *Out Of My Later Years,* p. 45).

Identifying gravitation with acceleration. But Einstein goes further than merely to state that bodies in a gravitational field behave *as if* they were in an accelerated system. He treats the two systems as if identical, saying, in effect, that a body that is in an accelerated system *is in* a gravitational field. Thus, in his discussion of the observer in the accelerated chest in empty space, he says (*Rel.* p. 82). "A gravitational field *exists* for the man in the chest." (Itel. ours.).

However, the language used by Einstein is not so important as the validity of the deductions Einstein makes from this language. So let us see how Einstein makes a deduction from his principle of equivalence regarding the bending of light rays in a gravitational field.

The bending of light rays in a gravitational field. Einstein would have us believe that the bending of light rays in a gravitational field constitutes a confirmation of the general theory of relativity. Thus, Appendix III of his *Relativity* is entitled The Experimental Confirmation of the General Theory of Relativity. In this appendix he says (p. 152) that "according to the general theory of relativity a ray of light will experience a curvature of its path when passing through a gravitational field." He cites the results of experiments revealing the bending of light rays in a gravitational field and says (p. 155), "The results of the measurements confirm the theory in a thoroughly satisfactory manner."

Violation of logic. Let the reader be reminded again that in making a statement of this sort Einstein is guilty of a flagrant violation of the established principles of logic. Any one familiar with logic knows that the confirmation of a consequence does not confirm the antecdeent.* Let us not be mislead, by Einstein's lacks of understanding of logic.

---

* For example, in the course of time bacteria sometimes develop a degree of immunity to a certain toxic substance. There are two theorites that are presumed to account for this phenomenon. One is the theory of the inheritnace of acquired characters. The other is the theory of evolution by the survival of the fittest.

According to the first theory the bacteria subjected to the toxic substance get used to it and as a consequence tend to have offspring that have more immunity than the preceding generation. According to the second theory whether the bacteria 'get used' to the toxic substance or not has nothing to do with the immunity of their offspring. According to this theory the offspring of a bacterium tend to be born sometimes with greater immunity and sometimes with less immunity by pure

Another theory explains the bending of light rays. In the statements quoted above Einstein implies that the bending of light rays in a gravitational field can be accounted for only by the general theory of relativity. But this phenomenon can be explained much more simply without any recourse to Einstein's principle of equivalence.

Numerous phenonmena, such as the Compton effect, have shown that photons have inertial mass. Hence we have merely to assume that the inertial mass of a photon is subject to the force of gravity and it follows that the path of a light ray will be bent in a gravitational field just as the path of a bullet fired horizontally would be bent downward by the force of gravity.

Indeed, Einstein, himself, gives this explanation. He says "A beam of light carries energy and energy has mass. But every inertial mass is attracted by the gravitational field . . . A beam of light will bend in a gravitational field exactly as a body would if thrown horizontally with a velocity equal to that of light." (Einstein and Infeld, p. 243).

It is shown, therefore, that the bending of light rays in a gravitational field can be accounted for entirely in terms of classical concepts.

However, it will be of interest to follow the reasoning by which Einstein presumes to show that the bending of light rays in a gravitational field is a consequence of the general theory.

Bending of a light ray in an accelerating system. In order to understand clearly Einstein's concept of the relation between the bending of light rays and the principle of equivalence, let us see just why the path of a light ray would be bent in an accelerating system.

Suppose a chest to be accelerated upward in the manner represented by diagram (*a*) in Fig. 1a. Let us suppose the chest, represented by the rectangle, to be in the position *AAAA* at instant i_0, to be in the position *BBBB* at instant i_1, in the position *CCCC* at instant i_2, etc., representing uniform acceleration.

Now let us suppose that a beam of light passes through the chest horizontally in a straight line as shown by the dots in diagram (*a*), the dots, *a,b,c,d,e,* representing the position of the beam at the successive instants i_0, i_1, i_2, i_3, and i_4.

chance; that the bacteria born in this way with the lesser immunity tend to die off in greater proportion when subjected to the toxic substance, thereby leaving that generation with a larger portion of immune bacteria. The same happens again each generation — the unfit die without leaving offspring, the fit survive and have offspring with a tendency for greater immunity.

Now the possession of greater immunity by one generation of bacteria than was possessed by the preceding generation is a consequence of each theory. But since the theories are mutually contradictory it is clear that the confirmation of the consequence cannot confirm both theories. Therefore it confirms neither. As was said, no theory is confirmed by the confirmation of its consequence.

Now the position of dot *a* relative to position *AAAA* of the chest at instant i_0 is shown by the dot *a* in diagram (*b*). The position of dot *b* relative to the position *BBBB* of the chest at instant i_1 is shown by the dot *b* in diagram (*b*), etc. And since these dots lie in a curve we know that the path of the beam of light through the chest when in acceleration would be curved.

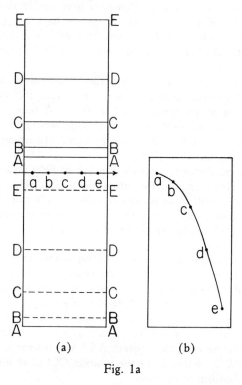

Fig. 1a

The bending of light rays and the principle of equivalence. Now let us see how Einstein makes it appear that the bending of light rays in a gravitational field depends upon his postulate of the general theory according to which bodies in a gravitational field behave as if they were in an accelerated system.

The reasoning consists merely in showing that a light ray projected horizontally through a chest (room) that is in upward acceleration would follow a curved path relative to the chest even in the absense of a gravitational field (which we have just seen it would) and then saying that since a gravitational field is the equivalent of a system in acceleration (or, more accurately, saying that since a gravitational field *exists* in the chest) a beam of light will therefore curve in any (other) gravitational field. Here are Einstein's statements that show this reasoning.

Einstein's statements. Einstein tells us (*Rel.* p. 87) that "the general principle of relativity puts us in a position to derive properties of the gravitational field in a purely theoretical manner." Then he supposes that a body of reference K' is in acceleration relative to a body of reference K, and tells us that because of this acceleration a gravitational field *exists* with respect to the body of reference K'. Then he says that a consideration of a process that would happen in a body of reference, such as K' that is in acceleration, would "teach us" how the gravitational field would influence that process.

He goes on to say (p. 88) that it can easily be shown that the path of a ray of light, when considered with reference to the accelerated chest (reference body K') is not a straight line, and says, "From this we conclude *that in general rays of light are propagated curvilinearly in gravitational* fields." (Ital. his).

Importance of the conclusion. Einstein goes on to say (p. 88) that the statement in italics just quoted is of great importance in two respects.

The first of these is that "it can be compared with reality." And he goes on to explain how the curvature of light rays in a gravitational field can be tested astronomically. Indeed, in a footnote (p. 89) he says that "the existence of the deflection of light *demanded by theory* was confirmed during the solar eclipse of 29th May, 1919." (Ital. ours).

We have seen however that this curving of light rays in a gravitational field is in no way dependent upon the Einstein theory of relativity, either special or general; and that even if it were a consequence of the general theory, as claimed by Einstein, the existence of the deflection of light would not confirm the theory because the confirmation of a consequence does not confirm the antecedent and because the phenomenon can be explained without recourse to an Einstein theory.

An evaluation of Einstein's reasoning may be had by a consideration of an imaginary point passing through a chest in acceleration. That is, let us suppose that instead of a beam of light, an imaginary point passes through the chest in acceleration in a straight line in the manner depicted in Fig. 1a. We know that the path of the imaginary point relative to the chest would be a curved line as shown in the figure. We cannot say that because of the similarity between gravity and the effect of acceleration it follows that an imaginary point passing through a gravitational field must of necessity follow a curved path. The imaginary point has no mass, either inertial or gravitational, so nothing could cause it to follow a curved path in a gravitational field.

This shows that the curvature of light rays in a gravitational field is wholly a matter of light possessing gravitational mass and has nothing at all to do with the equivalence of a gravitational field and a system in acceleration.

An analogy. We can characterize Einstein's reasoning by means of an analogy. We know that a horse and an elephant are alike in certain basic characteristics—each is a vertebrate, having four legs, etc., etc. Suppose we reasoned that because of this similarity between a horse and an elephant it follows that a horse IS an elephant, and that hence any characteristic of an elephant is also a characteristic of a horse, and that since an elephant has a trunk it follows that a horse also has a trunk.

That is the kind of reasoning Einstein uses in reasoning that (1) a body in acceleration is like a body in a gravitational field; hence (2) a body in acceleration *is in* a gravitational field; hence (3) any characteristic of a body in acceleration is a characteristic of a gravitational field; hence (4) light rays will bend in a gravitational field because they bend in a chest that is in acceleration.

We can dismiss this reasoning as fallacious.

Summary of chapter. In this chapter it was shown that a gravitational field and a system in acceleration are alike in certain respects (particularly in the way an observer would feel in each) but unlike in certain other respects (such as the direction of the forces and the variation of force with position). It was shown that in view of these similarities between the two systems and disregarding their differences Einstein reasoned that whatever happened to a light ray in a system in acceleration would happen to the light ray in a gravitational field and that consequently the bending of a light ray in a system in straight-line acceleration indicated that light rays would be bent in a gravitational field.

It was shown that by fallacious reasoning Einstein made it appear that the curvature of light rays in a gravitational field was a deduction from the general theory of relativity and that the discovery that light rays do bend in a gravitational field constitutes a confirmation of his general theory.

It was shown that it is possible to explain the curvature of light rays in a gravitational field in terms of purely classical concepts and that this curvature is therefore not in the least dependent upon the general theory.

We see, therefore, that Einstein's whole discussion of his 'principle of equivalence' came to naught. The curvature of light rays in a gravitational field was not a consequence of the theory and the observation of such curvature did not confirm the theory.

2a. THE CONCEPT OF SPHERICAL SPACE

Einstein's concepts. By means of a series of deductions Einstein concludes that "Our world is not Euclidean." (Einstein and Infeld p. 251). By means of an analogy Einstein reasons that the universe is finite but unbounded.

Purpose of the section. The purpose of this section is to examine the lines of reasoning by which Einstein arrives at the above conclusions as set forth in his *Relativity,* to which page references in the section relate.

It will discuss the illustration given by Einstein of a rotating disc and his reasons for considering that an observer on the disc would find that the ratio of the circumference of the disc to its diameter was not equal to *pi* (3.14159).

It will point out an error in Einstein's reasoning in consideration of which it will be clear that even according to the Einstein special theory the observer on the disc would find that the ratio in question *was* equal to *pi,* and that the conclusion drawn from the illustration is invalid.

It will discuss the analogy Einstein draws between a 'universe' consisting of the surface of a sphere and a universe consisting of 'spherical space', according to which he reasons that our universe is finite yet unbounded.

The rotating disc. In order to demonstrate that our world is not Euclidean, Einstein asks us to consider a large rotating disc (p. 94)*. We are to imagine an observer riding on the disc. The stationary system in which the disc is rotating is designated by Einstein as system K and the rotating disc is designated as system K'.

Although the rotating disc is unlike a gravitational field in several ways, Einstein reasons that the observer on the disc will consider the centrifugal force acting upon him as the effect of a gravitational field.

Measurements made on the disc. Einstein then reasons as follows regarding the measurement of the circumference and diameter of the disc by the observer on the disc.

According to Einsteins' special theory, if two inertial systems are in relative motion, a measuring rod lying in one of them in the direction of the relative motion will be contracted. Einstein regards a measuring rod lying in a circumferential direction on the disc as lying in

---

* See also Einstein and Infeld, p. 251.

the direction of its motion and considers that it will therefore be con tracted in accord with the special theory. He regards the measuring rod lying in a radial direction as not moving in the direction of its length and hence not contracted. Einstein says (p. 96), "If then, the observer first measures the circumference of the disc with his measuring rod and then the diameter of the disc, on dividing the one by the other, he will not obtain as quotient the familiar number $\pi = 3.14 \ldots$ but a larger number, whereas of course, for a disc which is at rest with respect to K this operation would yield π exactly."

In the foot note on that page Einstein states that relative to the disc "a gravitational field prevails." In other words, we are to consider that the disc, because of its rotation, is in a gravitational field. Einstein then says regarding the observer on the disc not getting *pi* for the ratio of the circumference to the diameter, "This proves that the propositions of Euclidean geometry cannot hold exactly on the rotating disc, nor in general in a gravitational field."

That is Einstein's reasoning by which he arrives at the conclusion that "Our world is not Euclidean."

Summarizing Einstein's reasoning. Briefly stated, Einstein reasons as follows. (1) Although the centrifugal force acting on the observer caused by the rotation of the disc is somewhat different from an actual force of gravity, nevertheless the observer would not be disturbed by this because he believes in the general theory of relativity. (2) Hence we are privileged to consider that the observer is in a gravitational field. (3) We, in our world, are in a gravitational field, hence whatever conditions the observer on the disc finds in his 'gravitational field' we will find in ours. (4) Since the observer on the disc would find, according to the special theory, that his system was not Euclidean, we must consider that "our world is not Euclidean."

The classicist's view of the reasoning. The classicist considers, of course, that the contraction of moving rods has been entirely discredited for reasons set forth in this booklet. Hence the classicist cannot even accept the premise upon which the reasoning is based. But let us consider the reasoning from the point of view of the Einstein special theory.

Analysis of Einstein's reasoning. Let us evaluate first the reasoning that led Einstein to conclude that the observer on the disc would find that the ratio of the circumference of the rotating disc to its diameter was not *pi*, as it would be if the disc were stationary. It will be shown that, according to the special theory of relativity, the observer on the rotating disc would find that the ratio of the circumference to the diameter *was* pi after all. Here is why.

117

According to the special theory any object that is 'in motion' is contracted in the direction of motion. This is true, according to the theory, whether the object be a meter rod, a cube, a sphere, a section of floor, or even an atom. (It will be remembered, for example, how Einstein agreed with Lorentz and FitzGerald that the arm of the interferometer in the Michelson-Morley experiment — which was in no way a measuring rod — would be contracted when lying in the direction of motion.) We may not assume that nature would make any distinction in the contraction of moving objects whether or not the object was to be used for measuring.

This means that in accord with the special theory (thinking of the disc as consisting of a number of concentric rings) each ring of the disc would contract because of its motion and a ring of the disc at any given distance from the center would contract in exactly the same degree as a measuring rod lying upon that ring would contract. If a meter rod on the circumference would contract to 99 cm., every meter of the circumference would likewise contract to 99 cm. Hence the contracted meter rod would be contained in the contracted circumference exactly the same number of times when the disc was in motion as the uncontracted meter rod was contained in the uncontracted circumference when the disc was at rest. That is, even according to the special theory, the observer would get the same measure of the circumference when the disc was in motion that he would get if it were at rest.

Hence, considering that Einstein assumes the observer would get the same value of the radius in both cases, we see that he would, of necessity, get the same ratio of the circumference to the diameter in each case. If he got *pi* when the disc was stationary, as he presumably would, then he would get *pi* when the disc was in motion.

It has been seen that the factor k in the transformation equation $x' = k (x - vt)$ makes it appear that when system S' is considered to be in motion relative to system S, any scale in system S' is either contracted or regraduated, as has been explained. We might think of the circumference of the disc as having been graduated when at rest to constitute a meter scale. The length of the circumference would then be shown by the reading at the end of the scale itself. (If the scale went from 0 to 10 this would show that the circumference was 10 meters long.) Now let us suppose the disc to be set in motion, and that when in motion it is contracted in accord with the Einstein concept of the contraction of moving objects. The contraction would in no way affect the scale readings — except to make the units shorter by contraction. If the scale read from 0 to 10 when at rest it would read from 0 to 10 when in motion. And this would still indicate to the observer that the circumference was 10 meters long — the same as before.

Hence Einstein's conclusion that the observer on the rotating disc, when dividing his measure of the circumference by his measure of the diameter, would obtain a quotient greater than *pi*, was an erroneous conclusion — even according to the special theory.

The classicist considers that the whole of Einstein's reasoning regarding our world not being Euclidean is fallacious and comes to naught because of this first error in reasoning.

A second fault. In regard to our world being non-Euclidean, we find a second fault in Einstein's reasoning in that even if the observer on the disc did find the ratio of the circumference to the diameter greater than pi, as Einstein said he would, this would prove nothing regarding a gravitational field. This is true for the same reason discussed in connection with the curvature of light rays. That is, in as much as the similarity between a system in acceleration and a gravitational field has been shown to be only a partial similarity, we are not permitted to conclude that whatever is true in the case of a rotating disc is also true in the case of a gravitational field. That kind of reasoning is like concluding that because Philadelphia is much like New York in many respects it follows that because New York has a harbor Philadelphia must have one also.

The finite but unbound universe. It appears that Einstein's argument leading to the conclusion that "our world is not Euclidean" was to serve as the basis for later reasoning leading to the conclusion that the universe is finite but unbounded.

Einstein says (p. 128), "The development of non-Euclidean geometry led to the recognition of the fact that we can cast doubt on infiniteness of our space without coming into conflist with the laws of thought or with experience."

He has us imagine some flat two-dimensional beings existing upon the surface of a sphere. He says, (p. 130) "The great charm resulting from this consideration lies in the recognition of the fact that the universe of these beings is finite and yet has no limits." He points out that on the spherical surface that constitutes the universe of the hypothetical flat beings geometry would not be Euclidean.

An analogy. Einstein draws an analogy between the 'universe' of the flat beings, which consists merely of the surface of a sphere and which he calls the "two-dimensional sphere universe", and the concept of a "three-dimensional spherical space." He points out (p. 131) that if the spherical-surface beings are living in a universe in which their habitable portion is but a small part, they would have no means of determining whether their surface was plane or curved. That is, they would not know that their surface curved off into a third dimension of space.

Einstein then explains that it is possible to imagine a spherical space. He implies that all we need to do is to imagine that there is a fourth dimension (although he does not mention it as such) into which our three-dimenional space can curve off in the same way that the two-dimensional surface of the sphere curves off into a third dimension of space. The three-dimensional space so curved off into a fourth dimension he calls "spherical space."

The analogy between the two-dimensional surface curving off into a third dimension and the three-dimensional space curving off into an implied but necessary fourth dimension is poorly drawn but it appears to be one in which Einstein compares lines on the surfa e of a sphere radiating from any point (like meridians radiating from the pole) to lines in the universe radiating in all directions from any point in the universe. We know that in the case of lines radiating from a point on the surface of a sphere the lines would diverge more and more until they reached an 'equator' and would then begin to converge and would eventually come together at a point at the other end of a diameter of the sphere. By analogy Einstein describes a corresponding concept of a universe in which straight lines radiating in all directions from a point would eventually converge. He conceives (p. 133) that "at first the straight lines which radiate from the starting point diverge further and further from one another but later approach each other, and finally they run together again at a 'counter point' of the starting point. Under such conditions they have traveled the whole spherical space." He then says, "It is easily seen that the three-dimensional spherical space is quite analogous to the two-dimensional spherical surface."

Closed space without limits. Einstein says (p. 133), "It follows from what has been said, that closed spaces without limits are conceivable. From amongst these, the spherical space (and the elliptical) excels in its simplicity, since all points on it are equivalent. As a result of this discussion, a most interesting question arises for astronomers and physicists, and that is whether the universe in which we live is infinite, or whether it is finite in the manner of a spherical universe. Our experience is far from being sufficient to enable us to answer this question. But the general theory of relativity permits of our answering it with a moderate degree of certainty." — implying, of course, in the affirmative.

Differing non-Euclidean characters. The non-Euclidean character of the rotating disc, according to Einstein, consisted in the fact that the observer on the disc would presumably find that the ratio of the circumference of the disc to its diameter was *greater* than *pi*. But flat beings residing on the surface of a sphere would find that the ratio of the circumference of a circle to its diameter (measured on the surface of the sphere) was *less* than *pi*. This shows, of course, that the non-Euclidean character of the spherical surface is of an entirely different kind from the alleged non-Euclidean character of the rotating disc. This fact in itself is sufficient to invalidate the whole line of reasoning.

What Einstein has done, therefore, is to reason that because a gravitational field is like a rotating disc and because we are in a gravitational field, our world must be like a rotation disc. He presumes to show that for the observer on the rotating disc the disc is not Euclidean, and then implying that anything that is not Euclidean must be spherical (in total disregard of the difference between the non-Euclidean character of a spherical surface and the presumed non-Euclidean character of the rotating disc), and treating the universe as if it were in a gravitational field, he arrives at the concept, possessing "great charm", that the universe must be a "three-dimensional spherical space".

Not a consequence of the theory. It must be realized that Einstein's analogy between the finite but unbounded character of the surface of a sphere and the finite but unbounded character of a hypothetical "curved space" has nothing to do with the concept called the principle of equivalence which is the basic postulate of the general theory of relativity. Hence Einstein's concept of 'spherical space' cannot be regarded as a consequence of the general theory, but merely as a disparate concept evolved by a purely imaginary analogy.

An unacceptable concept. Needless to say Einstein's concept of a curved space is unacceptable to the classicist and neo-relativist (1) because it is based upon an unacceptable concept of the contraction of moving objects, (2) because it is based upon the unacceptable concept that any character of a system in any kind of acceleration must of necessity be a character of a gravitational field, (3) because even the reasoning was found to be faulty because of the unlike non-Euclidean characters of the rotating disc and a spherical surface, (4) because the analogy upon which it is based is pure imagination, and (5) because the classicist and neo-relativist cannot imagine any fourth dimension of space into which our three-dimensional universe could curve off; nor can our three-dimensional space be conceived of as curving off into time — as a fourth dimension of space.

3a. EINSTEIN'S FOURTH DIMENSION

Gravity the result of curved space. It is considered by many to be impossible for gravity to be a force reaching out through space from a heavenly body to pull objects toward it. In an attempt to explain gravity without a concept of action at a distance it has been proposed that a gravitational field is like a vortex in a lake or a dimple-shaped depression in a flat level surface. The explanation of the action of gravity is then as follows.

Let us suppose we have a flat surface, which we may think of as a thin sheet of metal in which a depression has been pushed by a pointed object to form a 'dimple'. If we roll a marble across the outer portion of the depression the slant of the surface in the depression being toward the center will give the marble a tendency to roll toward the center (as it would if placed near the edge of the depression), this tendency being the effect of a centripetal force acting on the marble. This centripetal force on the marble will cause its path to be curved toward the center of the depression. Its path will be like the path of a comet approaching the sun from a distance but sweeping past it in a path that is curved toward the sun.

Also we can imagine the marble as p'aced in the outer portion of the depression and given a push at right angles to the direction of the center with just the right speed so that it will continue to roll around in the depression in a circle — simulating the motion of the moon around the earth.

The virtue of this imagery is that it portrays the marble as not pulled toward the center of the depression by any force of attraction of an object at the center of the depression. Hence the imagery presumes to show how a body can appear to be attracted toward a heavenly body without any action of the heavenly body pulling upon the body. That is, the force acting on the body is presumed to be acting right where the body is and not from a distance.

We have merely then to consider that the space around a heavenly body is 'curved' in order to imagine that some force could act upon the satelite of a heavenly body to represent gravity but to act only where the satellite is and not from a distance.

This reasoning is unsatisfactory because the centripetal force acting on the marble is the inward slanting component of a presumed downward force of gravity which itself must be acting from a distance. That is, although we have gotten rid of the need of a force acting from the center of the depression to pull the marble sidewise we have merely substituted a force acting from a distance to pull it downward and then used a component of this force to push it toward the center.

122

This means that to carry out the analogy we would have to imagine that in the case of the moon revolving around the earth, for example, the space around the earth was in a sort of gravitational field as if resulting from the presence of a ponderous body *below* the earth, so to speak, and that the seeming pull of the earth upon the moon was the earthward component of this downward slanting force of gravity caused by the 'curvature of space' and the resulting slant of space toward the earth.

It is seen that this reasoning merely eliminates the concept of the force of gravity acting at a distance from the earth by substituting the concept of a force of gravity acting at a distance from a body 'below' the earth. This reasoning does not eliminate the concept of action at a distance.

It will be realized, of course, that the kind of curvature of space that would form a 'dimple' in space around a heavenly body is entirely different from the kind inherent in Einstein's spherical space. The simple device of reasoning that our world is not Euclidean cannot be used as the basis for assuming space to be both spherical and dimpled.

The classicist considers, therefore, that the miscellaneous concepts of the curvature of space are wholly imaginary and not even related to the Einstein general theory postulate that a gravitational field is the equivalent of a system in either straight-line acceleration or the acceleration of revolution.

Indeed, it appears to the classicist that the so-called general theory of relativity consists of a mere aggregation of more or less unrelated concepts:

the relativity of uniform and accelerated motion,
the constancy of the velocity of light,
the 'equivalence' (identity) of gravity and acceleration,
the sphericity of space,
the dimpledness of space,
the four-dimensional space-time continuum.

The need for a fourth dimension. We have seen that in the case of the hypothetical world of flat beings imagined as living on the surface of a sphere and having only two dimensions in which to move even though their world was without boundary, this concept required, nevertheless, a third dimension of space into which the two-dimensional surface could 'curve off', so to speak, and become the surface of a sphere.

Similarly, in order to imagine a 'curved space' in accord with Einstein's concept of a universe in which lines radiating from any point in the universe could converge in a 'counter point', we would have to con-

123

ceive of a fourth dimension of space into which the three-dimensional space of which we are aware could 'curve off' to form a four-dimensional universe that is unbounded.

Preparing the reader. Presumably in order to persuade the reader that there is a possibility of such a universe Einstein includes a chapter in his *Relativity* entitled "Minkowski's Four-Dimensional Space." In his first paragraph he says: (p. 65) "The non-mathematician is seized by a mysterious shuddering when he hears of four-dimensional things, by a feeling not unlike that awakened by thoughts of the occult. And yet there is no more common-place statement than that the world in which we live is a four-dimensional space-time continuum."

Minkowski's four-dimensional space. It would seem that the idea of demonstrating mathematically that space has four dimensions arose in the mind of Minkowski, a contemporary of Einstein, who is credited with discovering that according to the transformation equations of the Einstein special theory

$$x'^2 + y'^2 + z'^2 - (ct')^2 = x^2 + y^2 + z^2 - (ct)^2 \qquad (1a)$$

from which he derived an equation in the form

$$x'^2 + y'^2 + z'^2 + w'^2 = x^2 + y^2 + z^2 + w^2 \qquad (2a)$$

in which x, y, z, and w, are presumed to be the four coordinates of a point in some four-dimensional inertial system S, and in which x', y', z', and w' are presumed to be the four coordinates of the same point in any other four-dimensional inertial system S'.

The meaning of equation (1a). To understand equation (1a) let us think of a point P coinciding with the origins O and O' of systems S and S' at an instant i_o at which these origins coincide. Let us think of the origin O' as moving to the right relative to origin O; and think of point P as moving uniformly in the direction indicated by the line OP in Fig. 3a, arriving at point P of the figure at an instant i_1.

In equation (1a) x, y, and z represent the coordinates of point P in system S, that is, as measured from origin O; and x', y' and z' represent the coordinates of point P in system S', that is, as measured from origin O'. For convenience the distances OP and $O'P$ have been designated as d and d' respectively.

We know, of course, that in this case $y' = y$ and $z' = z$.

In equation (1a) the symbol t represents the time it took point P to travel from the origin of system S to its position in the figure, as measured in system S; and t' represents the time it took point P to travel from O', as measured in system S' — it being presumed that t and t' do not come out the same.

124

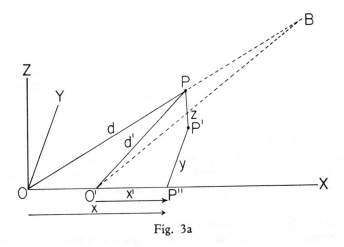

Fig. 3a

Since c represents the velocity of light, the term ct in the equation represents the distance OB that a beam of light could travel in the time t in system S; and ct' represents the distance that the same beam could travel in system S' in the time t'. Let us represent distances OB and $O'B$ by D and D', respectively.

So what Minkowski discovered, briefly stated, is that according to the transformation equations it will always happen that

$$d^2 - D^2 = d'^2 - D'^2 \qquad (3a)$$

An example. It can be shown numerically that equation (1a) is true according to the transformation equations. For example, suppose we let $c = 3$, $v = 1$, $t = 1$, $x = 2$, $y = 0$ and $z = 0$. In that case it follows immediately that the right member of equation (1a) $= -5$. That is, $x^2 + y^2 + z^2 - (ct)^2 = 4 + 0 + 0 - 9 = -5$.

It is then a comparatively simple matter to find the value of the left member, deriving x' from x and t' from t by the use of the transformation equations. In so doing it will be found that $x'^2 + y'^2 + z'^2 - (ct')^2$ also equals -5.

Both sides of equation (1a) must come out negative because a beam of light can always move farther in a given time than a point P moving with a velocity less than c. But it will be seen that Minkowski had a purpose in keeping the terms $-(ct)^2$ and $-(ct')^2$ in the last position on both sides of equation (1a).

It is conceivable that Minkowski, looking at the equation

$$x'^2 + y'^2 + z'^2 - (ct')^2 = x^2 + y^2 + z^2 - (ct)^2 \qquad (1a)$$

125

thought to himself: Wouldn't it be nice if we could in some way convert this equation into an equation reading

$$x'^2 + y'^2 + z'^2 + w'^2 = x^2 + y^2 + z^2 + w^2 \qquad (2a)$$

Then we could think of w as the fourth coordinate of point P in a 'space-time continuum' S, and w' as the fourth coordinate of point P in the corresponding space-time continuum S'. That would make it appear that the sum of the squares of the four coordinates of a point was a constant — the same in all inertial systems.

The use of imaginary numbers. Of course in the matter of converting the equation (1a) into equation (2a) Minkowski was confronted with a slight technicality which lay in the fact that he had to let the negative quantity $-(ct)^2$ be represented by the positive quantity w^2, in which case w would have to equal $\sqrt{-(ct)^2}$ or $\sqrt{-1}\, ct$. And similarly w'^2 would have to equal $\sqrt{-1\,(ct')^2}$ or $\sqrt{-1}\, ct'$.

Now we know, of course, that $\sqrt{-1}$ is a purely imaginary number because no real number multiplied by itself will give -1. But presumably Minkowski did not wish to let a mere technicality of that sort thwart his accomplishment. We can imagine his thinking: So what? I will just go ahead anyway.

So he let the imaginary number $\sqrt{-1}\, ct$ be considered the fourth coordinate (w) of point P in system S and let the imaginary number $\sqrt{-1}\, ct'$ be considered the fourth coordinate (w') of point P in system S'.

This means, of course, that the concept represented by equation (2a)—that the sum of the squares of the four coordinates of a point P at any instant are the same in any two inertial four-dimensional space-time systems (continua) — is a purely imaginary concept. Nevertheless if we feel the need for a four-dimensional space and wish to believe that it exists, equation (2a) lends a certain verisimilitude to that concept, and hence to the concept that space is curved.

So let us see what Einstein says about Minkowski's discovery and the four-dimensional space.

Einstein's comment on Minkowski's four-dimensional space. In as much as Minkowski's equation (1a) was based upon Einstein's transformation equations Einstein adopted Minkowski's concept of four-dimensional space (based upon his trick equation 2a), regarding it as a consequence of his theory. He says (p. 67) that the importance of Minkowski's discovery for the formal development of the theory of relativity "is to be found in the fact of his recognition that the four-dimensional space-time continuum of the theory of relativity, in its

126

most esssential formal properties, shows a pronounced relationship to the three-dimensional continuum of Euclidean geomethical space. In order to give due prominence to this relationship, however, we must replace the usual time coordinate t by an imaginary magnitude $\sqrt{-1}\ ct$ proportional to it. Under these conditions, the natural laws satisfying the demands of the (special) theory of relativity assume mathematical forms, in which the time coordinate plays exactly the same role as the three space coordinates. Formally, these four coordinates correspond exactly to the three space coordinates of Euclidean geometry. It must be clear even to the non-mathematician that, as a consequence of this purely formal addition to our knowledge, the theory perforce gained clearness in no mean measure."

To the classicist this means that by the mathematical magic of letting the imaginary quantity $\sqrt{-1}\ ct$ take the place of t, the usual time coordinate of an event becomes a space coordinate in a four-dimensional space — and that clears up everything!

Not a fourth coordinate. When equation (1a) was converted by Minkowski into equation (2a) by the mathematical trick of substituting w for $\sqrt{-1}\ ct$ and w' for $\sqrt{-1}\ ct'$ it was taken for granted that w, as a 'fourth dimension' or coordinate of point P, was an independent dimension or coordinate, just as the x, y, and z coordinates are presumed to be independent, each from the others.

It will be realized, however, that in the case of a beam of light
$$(ct)^2 = x^2 + y^2 + z^2$$
That is, the value of $(ct)^2$ depends entirely upon the values of x^2, y^2, and z^2, and hence is in no sense independent of these values.

This means that even if we write the equation of a beam of light as
$$x'^2 + y'^2 + z'^2 + w'^2 = x^2 + y^2 + z^2 + w^2$$
we still cannot regard either w or w' as a fourth space coordinate of point P. That is, after all the discussion of four dimensions of space, Minkowski and Einstein end up with only three dimensions of space.

No correspondence. It is interesting to speculate (1) as to why Minkowski should have wished in the first place to consider the equation
$$x^2 + y^2 + z^2 + w^2 = x'^2 + y'^2 + z'^2 + w'^2 \qquad (2a)$$
to be a true equation representing the concept that the sum of the squares of the four coordinates of a point in four-dimensional space is a constant — the same in both systems S and S' — when it is not true that the sum of the squares of the three coordinates of a point in a three-dimensional space is a constant; and (2) as to why Einstein, referring to the coordinates x, y, z, and w, should say that "Formally, these four coordinates correspond exactly to the three space coordinates

127

of Euclidean geometry," implying that equation (2a), considered as a true equation, corresponds exactly to the equation

$$x'^2 + y'^2 + z^2 = x^2 + y^2 + z^2 \qquad (4a)$$

considered as a true equation.

What purpose could Minkowski and Einstein have in mind considering equation (2a) to be a true equation when equation (4a) is not a true equation? The left side of equation (4a) is represented by the square of distance d in Fig. (3a) and the right side is represented by the square of distance d' in that figure. Certainly distances d and d' are not equal so of course the squares of these distances could not be equal.

The classicist cannot see any point in claiming that an equation presumed to be true regarding four-dimensional space corresponds exactly to an equation regarding three-dimensional space that is known to be false.

Contemporary opinion. In his book, *The Universe Around Us,* (1953) Sir James Jeans says (p. 78), 'In this new scheme, the phenomena of nature appeared as a picture painted in an entirely new space of four dimensions. This proved to be a purely mathematical and therefore probably a wholly fictitious space; in it the space and time of our every-day life were inextricably bound together into a new space of four dimensions, in which they then appear more or less as equal partners."

He says (p. 79), "This last multiplication by the square root of -1 is of course the remarkable feature of the whole affair. For the square root of -1 has no real existence; it is what the mathematician describes as an 'imaginary' number. No real number multiplied by itself can give -1 as the product. Yet it is only when time is measured in terms of an imaginary unit of $\sqrt{-1}$ years that there is true equal partnership between space and time. This means that the equal partnership is purely formal — it is nothing but a convenient fiction of the mathematician. Indeed, had it been anything more, our intuitive conviction that time is something different from space could have had no basis in experience and so would have vanished ere now."

Summary. The discussion of the fourth dimension of Einstein and Minkowski revealed the following.

1. There is no need for a fourth dimension of space except as we wish to explain the action of gravity without the concept of 'action at a distance' — that is, by means of concepts such as that the space around a heavenly body is 'dimpled'. And even the concept of dimpled space around a body still requires 'action at a distance'.

2. Minkowski derived an equation which purported to indicate that any point in the universe had four coordinates in an inertial system and that the sum of the squares of the four space coordinates of any point P is the same in any system as in any other system.

3. It developed that the derivation of this equation required the use of imaginary numbers; so that the derived equation itself was purely imaginary, having no correspondence with any reality.

4. It was found that what Minkowski and Einstein set forth as a fourth and hence independent coordinate of a point P turned out to be not an independent coordinate but merely a value dependent upon the values of the first three coordinates, leaving Einsten and Minkowski with only three dimensions of space after all.

5. The interpretation of Minkowski's equation — that the four coordinates of a point in space are such that the sum of the squares of the four coordinates of a point P are the same in any inertial system as in any other — implies that this is in accord with the fact that the sum of the squares of the three Euclidean coordinates of a point in any inertial system (S') is the same as the sum of the squares of the three Euclidean coordinates of that point in any other system (S). But it was found that this implication was false.

6. Sir James Jeans in 1953 saw the fallacy of Minkowski's reasoning.

7. The so-called general theory of relativity appears to be a collection of more or less unrelated concepts.

Summary of the discussion of the general theory. The three principal concepts set forth by Einstein in his *Relativity* regarding his general theory of relativity are:

1. The principle of equivadence (of acceleration and gravity).

2. The nonEuclidean character of the universe (space is curved and the universe is unbounded).

3. Space has four dimensions.

Einstein pointed out a few similarities between a body in acceleration and a body in a gravitational field and proceeded to state that a body in acceleration *is in* a gravitational field — that is, he says that when a body is in acceleration a gravitational field "exists". He then assumes that any characteristic of a body in acceleration is a characteristic of a gravitational field; and reasons therefore that because a beam of light passing through a chest in acceleration would follow a path that was curved relative to the chest, it must follow that a beam of light passing through a gravitational field would also be curved. The classicist cannot accept such reasoning.

And when all was said Einstein explained that "a beam of light carries energy and energy has mass" and that mass is attracted by a gravitational field — thus setting forth a complete and independent explanation of the curvature of light rays in a gravitational field and revealing that this phenomenon is in no way a consequence of the general theory, as implied in his discussion.

Einstein enunciates a concept of 'the curvature of space' which is invoked to explain the action of gravity without 'action at a distance', and to explain why our world is not Euclidean. The reasoning turned out to be fallacious because of the simple error of reasoning that in the case of a revolving disc an observer on the disc would find that the ratio of the circumference to the diameter was not pi; whereas it was found that even according to the theory of relativity the observer would still obtain pi (3.1416) as the ratio in question.

As for the concept of the universe as a 'four-dimensional space-time continuum' the attempt of Minkowski and Einstein to demonstrate this mathematically came to naught because it was based upon the use of imaginary numbers.

Except for the interesting observation that an observer in a chest that is in upward acceleration (in gravity-free space) would experience what he could easily mistake for a downward pull of gravity, the author sees no value in any of the discussion of the general theory in Einstein's *Relativity*.